REY LEAR

REY LEAR

THE TRANSCANTABRIAN

The Transcantabrian / First English-language Edition published by ChristieBooks
in conjunction with Rey Lear, April, 2008
(Published in Spanish as El Transcantábrico, *1982)*

REY LEAR, S.L.
www.reylear.com

ChristieBooks
PO Box 35, Hastings, East Sussex, TN34 2UX
christie@btclick.com

Distributed in the UK by Central Books Ltd
99 Wallis Road, London E9 5LN
orders@centralbooks.com
www.centralbooks.com

ISBN: 1-873976-33-X
ISBN-13: 9781873976333
P - 55 / 08

British Library Cataloguing in Publication Data.
A catalogue record for this book is available from the British Library

This book has been published with a subsidy
from the Dirección General del Libro, Archivos
y Bibliotecas of the Spanish Ministry of Culture

Impreso en la Unión Europea
Printed in E.U.

THE TRANSCANTABRIAN

Juan Pedro Aparicio

Illustrations by José S.-Carralero
& Maribel Fraguas

Translation by Michael Jacobs

FRAGUAS.

Índice

THE TRANSCANTABRIAN:
A JOURNEY ON THE 'COAL TRAIN'

*T*HE TRANSCANTABRIAN, one of the very few works of Spanish travel literature now available in English, deals appropriately with a Spain far removed from the sunny, sensual, and essentially Moorish land that foreigners still love to imagine. The railway line described here (and with such vividness that the book gave birth to a luxury tourist train

«The railway line described here is one of the most interesting in Europe, and yet one of the least known»

of the same name) is one of the most interesting in Europe, and yet one of the least known. Running from the industrial town of Bilbao to the capital of the ancient medieval kingdom of León, it goes through corners of northern Spain such as the Mena Valley that have remained barely spoilt ever since the work first appeared, nearly thirty years ago. Much of the landscape is greenly bucolic; but there are also parts of the route that are unforgettably bleak and even Nordic. On the grey June day when Juan Pedro Apa-

13

ricio did his minutely remembered journey, the desolation at one point is such that the author is a reminded of a short story by Kafka.

Aparicio's Spain has none of the conventional exoticism that travellers so often look for in this country; but few other recent accounts of Spain have captured so accurately (and wittily) the feel of the place.

Here is a Spain that is in many
ways unchanged—a country united
by such factors as a blind love for one's *pueblo*,
a passion for eating, and an ability to confide intimate
details of one's life to any passing stranger. But here
too is a Spain viewed at a key moment in its transition
to democracy—a country torn between an uncertain
future, and a past where emigration is the norm, where
memories of the Civil War remain intensely strong,
where a traveller's luggage consists mainly of food, and
where (at least as far as train travel is concerned)
there is a glorious lack of bureaucratically imposed
safety regulations.

Though the landscapes and architectural
attractions of northern Spain are well conveyed both

15

in the text and in the delicate illustrations by José S.-Carralero and Maribel Fraguas, the great achievement of this book lies in its description of people, who are rendered with unfailing sympathy, no matter if they are boring, pedantic, pretentious, or downright deranged. Above all there is the train driver Chuchi, whose personality becomes confused in the end with that of the train itself. Impetuous, individualistic, eccentric, bloody-minded, falling apart, and deeply vulnerable, both Chuchi, and the train he drives, are the ultimate symbols of a vanishing Spain that is evoked here with a rare combination of humour, poignancy and humanity.

MICHAEL JACOBS

THE TRANSCANTABRIAN

Juan Pedro Aparicio

For Isabel

CONCORDIA COMES IN THREES

BILBAO, JUNE 6, 1980, shortly before eight in the morning. You still cannot tell how the day is going to turn out. The sky, with its flat, grey clouds, seems undecided. There is a paleness about the light, threatening perhaps a Scotch mist; but there is also an incipient glow crowning the background mountains, appearing to denote hope. Perhaps this uncertainty is a sign of the times.

«Concordia –what a wonderful name for a station, and in Bilbao of all places!–»

Concordia—what a wonderful name for a station, and in Bilbao of all places!— is a true railway trinity: three different stations, three tracks, and even three different railway lines; and yet only one true station. From Concordia depart the RENFE trains; as do the narrow gauge trains that go their separate ways to Santander and León; from Concordia too —or rather from immediately outside— leave Bilbao's suburban trains, which run almost hidden under what looks like a great step on the Nervión's embankment.

The building was constructed by the architect Severino Achúcarro in the expanding, turn-of-the-19th-century Bilbao known to Unamuno. It has all the characteristics of those years, and has much in common with the stations and market buildings that grew up all over Europe during that time.

What stands out is the central arch, which, like a coloured stele flanked by stained glass, crowns the frontispiece of the façade, turning its large clock into a truly eye-catching feature, rather like a rising sun, or the centre of an altar, a place both esoteric and mesmerizing, emitting golden rays. Sadly, the clock is stuck at twenty past ten, twenty past ten of God knows what year.

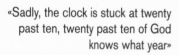

«Sadly, the clock is stuck at twenty past ten, twenty past ten of God knows what year»

Below the clock, as if to underline the fact that time has stopped, can be read the words: Bilbao-Santander. And yes, the name León does not appear. There is some explanation for this, if a rather involved one: the original railway line, founded to transport coal from León to the iron and steel works of Bilbao (hence the nickname of *'El Hullero'*, the 'Coal Train'), did not stop at Bilbao, but rather ran alongside the River Cadagua until this reached the sea at Luchana, which even today is the terminal for cargo trains. Only a later agreement with a Santander company (likewise owned today by the

Bkeish
FRAGUAS.

24

State-run FEVE —Ferrocariles Españoles de Vía Estrecha, or Spanish Narrow Gauge Railways)— allowed our line the use of Concordia.

And Concordia is where we now are. From the ticket office, where the name León is hand-written on a board, a long queue winds its way around the station's iron columns. A little man, in a beret, waistcoat and dark suit whose turn-ups spill over his shoes, is asking a question:

"Who's last?", he asks, tautening his body, puffing out his chest, heightening his voice, contorting his face. He's not really asking, he's challenging.

"Come on, let the last person step forward!", says the old man, made more irritated than ever by the lack of any reply.

However, it's not really surprising that no-one wants to come forward, fearful of the fury that admitting to "It's me!" might unleash.

Curiously, the queue, though big, is not chaotic, but extremely orderly, so that you can easily tell who's first and who's last. When the man, a truly strong personality, finally realizes how superfluous his question is, how the silence speaks for itself, he feels obliged to explain his behaviour.

"You see, I'm a fair man. I don't want to barge into a queue, nor I do want anyone barging in front of me".

The storm abates. Fernando goes off to take some photos of the station while I await my turn in the ticket queue.

The ticket from Bilbao to León costs 670 pesetas in First Class, and 485 in Second. According to the ticket seller, most of the long distance travellers go only as far as Guardo. "To León, there's only about one passenger a day, if that".

The platform is on a second floor, reached by a side staircase. A wide glazed canopy protects the two tracks from the elements. The canopy, light and delicate, is supported by ironwork columns running parallel to a large balcony that overlooks the Nervión, and which —when seen from outside, with its more than twenty concrete columns — lends to Concordia the air of some Acropolis.

A Vision of the Hullero

W E MEET UP IN THE MIDDLE of the platform with the guard, who is standing talking with three men. All four of them are wearing a jacket, dark blue trousers, and a railway worker's cap. The guard carefully reads the letter from the director of FEVE, which grants me permission to travel in the locomotive cab and the goods van, should I so wish, but 'under his

«The train —or should I say convoy?— is divided up into one first class carriage, four second class ones»

own responsibility insofar as he is not covered by the compulsory insurance to which every passenger is entitled'. The guard thinks of us as 'friends of the railway', and assumes we have done this several times before, "just like those who are always finding some interesting locomotive in Cistierna, and are photographing every old carriage…"

The director of the FEVE recommended to me the ham from Cabañas de Virtus, which he had always eaten in sandwiches ordered by telephone from Bilbao. However, Cabañas is no longer the

place it was. The guard is surprised by my not knowing this.

"In Cabañas everything has closed down."

His surprise at my ignorance is echoed by the others.

"There's no-one there anymore. The best place to eat is Mataporquera. We stop there for half an hour…"

The guard is the one who dominates the conversation. When speaking, air escapes from his mouth, as if he is missing a few teeth; this makes him appear older than his companions. Everyone is from León, except the one who is from Mataporquera, but he lives in Cistierna, just like the guard.

The train —or should I say convoy?— is divided up into one first class carriage, four second class ones, the goods van, and the engine car. The engine is Diesel. Who does not remember those steam engines that used to take us as schoolchildren from León to the mountains of La Vecilla? They were almost human in the way they moved - panting heavily, and exuding bad breath, like imprisoned dragons whose destinies had been chained to the rails for the betterment of mankind. An engine of that kind still runs between Villablino and Ponferrada.

However, our own train does not let us down. It's there waiting for us alongside the platform, its bent back displaying its old and familiar ribcage, like that of a horse meekly awaiting the weight of the rider. The Hullero is really a toy, a broken toy. The engine is blue and blunt, with none of that human physiognomy typical of those of steam trains. But its carriages have not changed a bit, and could well have been kidnapped by aliens some twenty years ago, and then returned, in one of Concordia's 'close encounters of the third kind.' For, as we have already said, everything in Concordia comes in threes.

All the coaches have a tiny, enclosed standing area at either end, and are marked on the outside by a date, which —we suspect— is not that of their construction, but rather that of their umpteenth repair, modification, or re-conversion. The first class carriage, green, quite elegant, and clearly pleased with itself, displays the date 1959. The second class carriages, in a weathered and rusty brown, and welded together by a steel similar to that used in the Cuban war, bears a slightly later date: 1960.

We are convinced we have seen this train before, as the setting for Ana Belén's television portrayal of the fictional heroine Fortunata. But apparently we are wrong. The guard, a native of León like us, with his dark black moustache, rounded face, and adolescent voice, now puts us right:

"Here they filmed 'Prisoners' Rope'—the adverb 'here' takes on the character of a noun, the 'here' being the train, the La Robla Railway, no matter where it is— "and they also filmed 'Sister Citroën'".

The guard asks us to accompany him to the engine
car. He wants to introduce us to the driver. While
we are walking there, he tells us:

"The train was absolutely packed when it set
off yesterday. Being a public holiday, there were ten
coaches, completely full."

Another of the railway workers —the one from Mataporquera— comes with us. He is shorter in build, and has a high-pitched voice. The bagginess of his clothes, and the wobbling of his double chin give an overall impression of flabbiness that is highlighted by the swish of his canvas shoes.

"Yesterday would have been a perfect day to research an article."

Some of the passengers, now settled in their seats, watch us from behind the windows, which makes us feel as if we are inspecting the carriages, escorted by two uniformed men.

To be honest, the Hullero is not any old train service. If the Transiberian spans a quarter of the world's surface —a far longer distance than that between New York and Madrid, should such a journey be possible

«All the coaches have a tiny, enclosed standing area at either end»

by train— our own railway, modest, long-suffering, and neglected, is the longest narrow gauge one in western Europe. The line extends for 340 kilometres.

The Transiberian and the Transcantabrian: that is a good comparison, rather like Goliath and David, with all due respect to the inhabitants of Spain's northern coast. The former goes across Siberia; the latter crosses the Cordillera Cantábrica, rocked between its ridges, galloping along its foothills.

Work on the Transiberian was begun in 1891 and completed in 1905. Of course, our David was swifter to complete; given the go ahead in 1891, the line was opened in 1894, the same year the Basque National Party, the PNV, was founded. Everything was done at record speed, which was remarkable given the area's rough terrain.

The first locomotive to run along its tracks was an 0-2T, built by the Franco-Belgian company La Croyère. It was given the name *'León'*. Modern times have now done away even with these names. The locomotive awaiting us, a blue 'Diesel', with nautical portholes on its sides, is identified simply by the number 1.160.

The train driver is a slight and vivacious man.

«The railway workers invite us to come and join them at Mataporquera for a "coal pot"»

"Come up to the cab whenever you like", he tells us, before adding the warning, "But I'm only going as far as Valmaseda. From there onwards there'll be a yellow engine."

Curiously, the guard warns us about this almost simultaneously.

"Of course, this is only going as far as Valmaseda, you realize that?"

The driver is called Enedino, another of the funny names that everyone here seems to have. We have no other choice but to ask him if he too comes from León. And yes he does. From Cistierna.

"That shouldn't surprise you. If you come from

an area with little industry, you're forced to emigrate to a place where there's work."

Enedino has the voice of a priest, so powerful that it seems as if it is a force being expelled outwards by his impressively sized Adam's apple. He is also someone with a precise manner of speech, and recommends that we come and see him in the cab when we reach Aranguren.

The railway workers, after a brief private consultation, invite us to come and join them at Mataporquera for a "coal pot".

"A *coal pot?*"

"And why not?", says the guard, "It's very cold here in winter. You need to eat something heated over coals."

He suggests that we leave our luggage in the goods van and urges us now to take our seats. The driver then goes up to say something to him. The guard listens, while continuing to look at us. He issues the same warning as before.

"In Valmaseda there's going to be a change of driver, but he's a good lad too. You'll be alright."

FRAGUAS.

Just like a Western

W E ENTER THE FIRST CLASS carriage. The passengers who were watching us parading down the platform in the company of the railway workers, look at us with curiosity.

The carriage interior is itself worthy of attention. With its spacious light blue seats topped by immense, baroque-crested headrests, its three-

«Its spacious light blue seats topped by immense, baroque-crested headrests»

bulb ceiling lights framed by massive metallic rings studded at their base with gold panels, and its green check curtains, the whole thing seems straight out of a Hollywood set.

The aisle divides the carriage into two seats on one side, and a single seat on the other. We sit in the opposite direction to the one in which the train will move. In front of us is a lady, and on the other side of the aisle is a middle-aged couple. The women must be getting on into their mid forties; the man must be well into his fifties.

It's a quarter to nine. The train's sudden start is quite memorable. A violent clashing of iron seems to issue from the train's entrails, just like the hiccup of a giant who is holding us in his gullet. One jolt, then another, then a third! That's quite enough! We can't help laughing. Our travelling companions do so as well.

"It's a miracle", says the woman who's part of the couple, "that we're actually leaving on time. And it's a miracle everything's so clean. If it gets like this to its destination, no-one will recognize it. In winter there's not even any heating, and now…"

The train pulls out of the station, making the classic stereotypical sound of departure. It seems to be beginning its journey with an unexpected surge of power. Then immediately it enters a tunnel, and the light acquires a somber hue.

The lady in front of us, whose short plump limbs suggest a great ball of energy contained within an overall gentle disposition, is going to Cistierna. The other, more slender woman, is going to Cillamayor.

"I never take this in the winter", says the latter, whose jollity has been growing in tandem with the train's gathering speed. "I would do so if the service were better, even if it were more expensive. If it were a service like the Cantábrico. Now they have much better trains."

Her companion, who is presumably her husband, and is sitting in front of her, and adjacent to us, now turns away from the newspaper he is holding to look in our direction, and smile at us with his eyes, without saying a word. He has a white face and the whitest and most mellow of moustaches.

The train carries on regardless, and has turned into a veritable rooster, crowing away, and announcing to the world that "I am here!"

"This'll stop soon", the two women say with patient smiles. And, as if in response to this, the train whistles again with even greater strength than before, with as much joy as it can muster. But this time the woman who is going to Cillamayor has had enough.

"This is just like a Western; all we need if for some Red Indians to attack us". Her husband continues looking at us with an expression of meek delight. "But have you been in the third class compartment?" And without waiting for us to reply, she concludes with a great peal of laughter. "But I suppose it's alright if you're young."

"The coaches are really uncomfortable", butts in the other woman, "they date back to before the war. This one at least was re-decorated in 1959. But the others were always like that. Where on earth did they find them?"

"In the Wild West", says the woman opposite, "you just have to look at all its dents."

"But, this coach is not bad at all, really".

"But it's still straight from the Wild West.

Don't you remember those coaches?... How should I describe them?... The ones in which the bosses used to travel!" The train makes some sudden jolts. "And at least this driver seems to be the one who has passed his test, because there are others who reach this point who..."

The woman who is going to Cistierna agrees. She appears to have greater experience of the matter:

"Yes, this is the driver who is going to Valmaseda. This one's as smooth as can be. Oh! He's as smooth as a mouse. The other one, in contrast... And when the goods get derailed, and they're the ones that matter, we are forced to change compartment, and no-one could care less that we're holding first class tickets. We're just shoved into third class, and that's the end of that..."

The other woman adds gleefully:

"Well, if this driver's like a mouse, the one who takes over at Valmaseda is a tiger. If that's not being too kind to him."

The woman who's going to Cistierna keeps on talking.

"Because I live in Eibar, I've got no choice in the matter, I'm obliged to take this train. But, don't get me wrong, this is a really useful service. How else could I get to Cistierna without it? If I used the line that goes to the north, I would have to change in Venta de Baños, and then again in León, where I would have to continue to Cistierna either by this train or by bus. That's why we have to defend this service. Two or three years ago, when there was talk of closing it down, everyone in Cisterna went on protest."

«The train is now running only a few metres above the estuary of the Nervión»

The train, which has still not gone beyond the city's limits, is now running only a few metres above the estuary of the Nervión, which is as smooth as a mirror. And, despite the water's dirtiness, its black depths reflect a broad horizon of ports, cranes and seagulls. But then immediately these maritime scenes are frustratringly dissolved, for while the estuary continues towards the sea, the Hullero turns its back on it in a sudden swerve that abruptly separates the train from this vision of water.

José P. Carralero.

VIZCAYA'S GREATEST TREASURE

Zorroza is the first station. Soon the train gets going again; but has hardly the time to gather any speed before it stops once more.

"What station is this?"

"Santa Agueda", the two women answer in unison.

Immediately, through the same window through which the estuary has just been seen (on the right of the train), appears the River Cadagua, which is revealed as a sad and miserable river staining the banks with its waters.

«Soon the train gets going again; but has hardly the time to gather any speed before it stops once more»

On the other side of the river are the mountains of Triano, most of them being too far away to be visible: Argalorio, Bitarratxu, Mendíbil, Pico Ventana, Peña Pastores, Ezkatxabel, Pico Mayor, Pico Menor, Ganeram, Gasteram, Pico La Cruz, Aldape, Eretza.

From these mountains came the greatest —and almost only— treasure of Vizcaya: iron. Most of the Vizcayan ironworks were in Triano. To this day there

"Los montes Trianos"
FRAGUAS

still remain the ruins of dams, massive walls, and slag heaps - the remains of ironworks that, for many centuries, were Vizcaya's most important industry (and one that was even responsible for the swords Shakespeare referred to as 'bilbos').

According to Néstor de Goicoechea in his book Mendigoizale, iron was extracted and fashioned in the following way:

'Many of the hills and other places in these provinces are rich in iron. Numerous cartloads of stones and earth from these sites are transported to the place where the foundry is situated, where they are then burnt with a great amount of coal and at a very high heat. The earth melts and makes a type of paste, which is then fashioned and turned into bars of such paste. Steel is made in the same way, but the earth required for it is finer than the other. The hammers used in this process are not wielded by hand. Instead, mallets operated by water wills are what soften the pastes to the required consistency.'

«On the other side of the river are the mountains of Triano, most of them being too far away to be visible»

But these Vizcayan ironworks would have been insignificant had it not been for the estuary. This is not just the present author's opinion. Miguel de Unamuno says that 'the true source of Bilbao's importance is its estuary, the Nervión, nerve centre of its commerce, the true father of the city. It alone explains the history of Bilbao.'

And Unamuno is extremely acute when he writes about his native city. For instance, he says, 'What would mines, such as those of Triano, be worth had they been in La Mancha? The estuary has saved on the vast amount of prior investment that would have been necessary before exploiting the mines. And the reason for this could not be simpler: the riches reaped from the mountains can go straight to the barges, which are just a few steps away.'

So acute is Don Miguel that much of his writings could well serve as a spiritual guide to Basque nationalists:

'We can therefore conclude', he continues, 'that all this is a gift from nature, and that the earth has made us what we are, and not vice a versa. Some of the most penetrating British authors, including Macaulay, were right when they attributed the prosperity of their land and even the character of its inhabitants to Britain's position as an island and to its deposits of coal, neither of which are the work of man, just as neither are the estuary nor the mountains of Triano.'

Mines such as those of Triano. How much would they be worth in La Mancha? And how much in León? I think that some of those travelling on this train might have an answer to this last question. But whatever the answer, one thing is clear: the investment in a narrow-gauge railway, this particular one, has for nearly a century, day after day, month after month, taken away the riches from the mines of León and Palencia to feed other and faraway industries.

FROM IRAUREGUI TO ZARAMILLO

THE COAL TRAIN HAS STOPPED in Irauregui. The Cistierna woman says to us:

"Most of those who come from Riaño and Cistierna have to emigrate to Bilbao. I've got two brothers here, but I have my own house. I've been living for ten years in Vizcaya."

The starting up of the train is more abrupt than ever, and takes us by surprise. The woman going to Cillamayor is in her element.

«The Cadagua is now on the left-hand side, horrible, dirty, with huge patches of scum forming into sinister white pools»

"If there's anyone here prone to travel sickness…"

Her husband looks at us, from his hiding-point of silence, a hint of malice flashing across his eyes.

Outside, the urban world is invading the rural one in a hybrid fashion. Great housing blocks, square, solid, and squat, rise up amidst rustic walls painted with political slogans. Above and behind the blocks, the green forms of the Triano mountains emerge from behind a turbulent mass of grey clouds that come together and swell like waves.

The Cadagua is now on the left-hand side, horrible, dirty, with huge patches of scum forming into sinister white pools in which float trees that have been torn at their roots, and are coated in mud.

Incongruous amidst all this filth is a chalet with a tiny swimming pool, a pool which is elongated like a bread roll, crushed below the train embankment on one side, and well placed on the other to breathe in the rising smells of the Cadagua.

The train whistles, and noticeably reduces its speed before just reaching Zaramillo. The Cistierna woman knows exactly what's happening.

"We're waiting here until the Santander train passes."

I get up to walk to the standing area at the back, where Fernando is taking some photos. The train suddenly shakes, forcing me to hold on to the wall. And then, as if as a consequence of this violent movement, the connecting door between the carriages opens, and out comes the guard. He's like an apparition. Effortlessly, and diligently, he removes the key to the lock and, as if he were St. Peter, places it in his trouser pocket.

While he punches the tickets of the other travellers, we walk down to the standing area at the other end of the carriage, where we find three young women. Two are blonde, short-haired, and not big at all (in fact, one of them is decidedly short), but strongly built and plump. The other woman, younger than the others, has long chestnut hair, and is tall and very beautiful.

The Cadagua still flows to our left. It arouses pity and aversion.

The guard sells the brunette her ticket, because there's no ticket office at the place where she's got on.

"It's just a halt stop, and they don't usually give out tickets there", he says.

The poplars along the Cadagua's banks have smooth, dark trunks, and their branches are almost horizontal. All the filth from the river gathers at their trunks, dressing them in nauseating rags. To make matters worse, the sky has become heavy and leaden.

"It'll clear as we go along. It'll be completely sunny by the time we reach Mataporquera. And now, if you'll excuse me, I'm going to have to check your ticket. There's going to be an inspector getting on. He's a very nice person, and all that, but he is someone who likes things to be done properly."

His duty done, we were hoping for him to take out the key from his pocket and continue his walk through the Hullero. But the train, which still has not reached the station of Zaramillo, has come to a stop, and so too has the guard.

The three young women have joined together as a group, and are chatting among themselves, softly, intermittently, with long pauses in which they try and make out what we are saying — pauses broken only by the odd sigh, and monosyllabic utterances that could almost be sighs.

The guard is enlightening us with details about cargo transport.

"The cargo we carry comes principally from Guardo, La Robla and Arija. From here downwards the containers travel almost empty. You virtually never get a full cargo train travelling in this direction. In contrast, travelling the other way, you get 10,000 tons a month, even from Sabero to La Robla. Impressive, eh? The coal is all distributed in Madrid. Yes, you know, what's his name, that person from Madrid, the one who's got his finger in every pie; the one who distributes the coal to all the power stations? From Sabero they're mining more coal than ever before, two thousands tons of the stuff. They're clearing the whole bloody mine."

The whistle of the approaching train can now be heard.

"It's because they're repairing one of the tracks. There's only one track now, and the other train is coming."

One of the three women now joins in.

"The maroon one."

"What did you say?", I ask.

"The maroon train is coming", explains the one who has spoken.

"You mean, it's painted maroon?"

"No", says the guard, "It comes from Marrón."

"No", says the taller of the two blondes, "that's from Santander".

We are now completely lost.

"If it really was the maroon train we'd be stuck here for ages", comments the guard.

"Where is Marrón?"

"In Santander", answers one of the women.

"It comes from there then?"

"No, no", says the woman, "it comes from Santander. They put on a coach from Marrón to Bilbao. There are two or three coaches which go from Marrón to Bilbao. But from Santander the other train leaves at ten thirty."

"And they join up?"

"The one coming from Santander is the other train. We pass it at Zaramillo."

«They're already doing something, laying out new tracks and sleepers»

We give up.

"But this is the Zaramillo one!"

The maroon train passes the Hullero to the right, untying the Gordian knot we have got into by its noise. The maroon train is a blue tram, new, metallic, clean and shining. We comment on it favourably. The brunette says:

"The one we're on is just a museum piece."

The guard comes to the defense of the weaker train.

"They've got to spend some money on this.

They're already doing something, laying out new tracks and sleepers. They've even bought some new engines."

The Hullero whistles.

The guard finishes what he was saying.

"But this never fills up with passengers."

The starting up of the train is more violent still, quite out of the ordinary. As we have the guard with us, we ask him why this should be. The women laugh just as if we had told the funniest of jokes. The guard replies in a resigned and serious tone, with the slight, irritated manner of someone who has to explain the obvious for the umpteenth time. He does this with the aid of surprisingly expansive gestures, which try and reproduce with his hands the train's workings.

"The whole thing has suffered too many bumps, and the buffers are all loose. Yes, it's all worn down! And when we have to go backwards, the train's response is much, much worse."

I touch the door cautiously, making the women burst into laughter again. The ticket collector says:

"You can lean on it without fear, it opens inwards. There's nothing to worry about."

We arrive at Zaramillo. Fernando walks down the coach again to stand at the back, The two blondes get off.

Dark Eyes

THE TALL, YOUNG AND BEAUTIFUL woman is left on her own, leaning on the wooden paneling, facing backwards.

The guard encourages her to sit down, "because there's still some way to go before Mercadillo".

"No, it's not that far. I'll get there at quarter to eleven, isn't that so?"

"It's thirty eight kilometers from Irauregui", says the guard.

"Bah! I'm quite used to that. For me it's nothing."

I ask the young woman if she knew the Hullero when its engines ran on steam. But it's the guard who answers me.

"Of course, I've known the train all my life. I've been forty five years in Cistierna, how am I not going to know it? And I come from a place only fifteen kilometers from there, Cerezal de Guzpeña, in between Prado and Puente. I was born there. I was in León for four years, got married, and then I came here, to Valmaseda.

The guard is of medium build, strong, and, without being actually fat, is quite burly. He must be well over fifty. The guard confuses his own life with that of the railway.

Every so often the Hullero passes under small stone bridges, with elegantly curved parapets, over which grows moss and honeysuckle.

"I began in Rail Maintenance", continues the guard, in a way which makes you want to relate his words to his uniform, which is so inseparable from his whole person that it almost grows on him like a second skin as the story unravels of his railway career.

"That's how you usually begin in this business: working on the tracks. Then, if there are any fixed posts, you apply for them, and take your exams. I went on to Works and Maintenance, and then I came to Cistierna, passed my exams to become a freight clerk, got a house, and stayed here."

But my role as author of this journey, as an observer of my fellow travellers, makes me duty bound to bring the young woman into the conversation. So, now that I know the guard's background, I ask her about hers.

"I'm from Alonsótegui", she answers.

The young woman has a lovely face, a body like that of a shop dummy —somewhat slumped, in need of exercise— and eyes that are dark and deep, calm and serene.

The author, a typical male after all —like the guard— wants to find out more about the young woman. And he tests his rod in waters he suspects to be unpromising. He asks the young woman if she likes Alonsótegui.

"I love the place more than anything", says the young woman, displaying for the first time some evidence of passion.

The Cadagua persists in showing signs of its decline. A magnificent poplar, like a dethroned monarch, stands half-collapsed, exposing its roots. White foaming scum turns the water into a river of beer. A lump of sadness forms in the author's throat. The young woman perceiving this perhaps, lets out a sigh. She says:

"It's always like this."

It is as if the author and the young woman have momentarily understood each other. She wants to add something:

«It's the paper factory that messes it all up. And when the river's low the water's all red»

"I had a friend…"

But it's the guard who speaks once more:

"It's the paper factory that messes it all up. And when the river's low the water's all red."

The young woman laughs.

Behind the poplars, and almost entwined with them, are clusters of beeches running parallel to the river.

The guard does not go away. What is more, he cannot keep quiet.

"Look over there!", he says suddenly, pushing his arm, with its index finger outstretched, in front of

"... Papelera que ensucia el Cadagua..
/osé Caballero .

my nose. "It's the other line! The earlier one, the one that went south from Valmaseda! Do you see it? Where those posts are!"

The author leans on the emergency brake, which is like a small iron wheel. And then immediately he jumps back as if he had burnt himself. While the young woman smiles, the guard reassures me once again:

"Don't worry, you'd have to turn that many times for the train to brake. There's one in every carriage."

The author, who still has not lost all hope of getting into conversation with the woman, makes a renewed attempt. He asks her if she speaks Basque. She says no. Then he asks her if they speak Basque in her village.

«To the left, not far from the track, is a large farmhouse resembling an old palace»

"No... no; in my village there's no-one who... from here onwards most people don't."

But, almost as she speaks, the guard enlightens me on the matter.

"It's more around San Sebastián and around there that they speak the language."

Then the young woman adds:

"No, in these villages, no. Perhaps, the old person..."

The Hullero stops in Sodupe. To the left, not far from the track, is a large farmhouse resembling

El caserón de Sodupe
Joni Cavaler

an old palace. The guard goes inside the coach to punch the ticket of someone who's just got on. A flicker of hopes lights up the author's heart. And in that moment he discovers that the young woman is called Alicia, that her life, as in the song, is led in between Alonsótegui and Bilbao, that she has not been to León.

But the guard comes back to say something that's obviously been on his mind:

"Yesterday, they brought in some of those big coaches. There was a lot of staff. People could have queued up to write articles. Sundays never fail, there are always lots of mountaineers."

The author sighs. Then she asks Alicia if she has one of those unusual Basque surnames that are so difficult to pronounce.

Alicia's paternal name is García and her maternal one is Bilbao.

The guard exclaims:

"I too am called García, but on my mother's side! Luis Oslé García."

But that's not all:

"My father's surname is really unusual: Oslé."

The author, had he wanted to be witty, would have shouted out "olé!". But he says nothing.

"What sort of surname is that?", asks the young woman.

"It's German", explains the guard, and he repeats it again slowly, enunciating each syllable, "Os-lé.

It's said in our family that there were two brothers who came over a long time ago from Germany when there was a war there. One remained in Reinosa, and the other came here, to León, and had offspring."

"In Alonsótegui there are many Basque surnames", says the young woman, clearly inspired by what she has just heard, "but there are also a lot of people from elsewhere."

Alonsótegui seems so cut off from the hurly burly of the real world that the author thinks it unlikely that the problems of the Basque Country have got there.

"A bomb went off recently in a bar, killing four people", says the young woman, proving the author to be wrong.

"They wrote about it in the newspapers", comments the guard.

"And it was on the television as well", adds the woman.

The author, with such a long way still to go, loses heart. He knows he'll never be able to talk to the woman without the guard intervening. He abandons the idea of doing so, relaxes, and then asks the guard if he sees the young woman every day.

"I've been doing this journey for about four months", she says.

The guard looks at her. He looks as well towards the main section of the coach. The author attempts to humour him. He says:

"You must know a lot of the people who take the train every day."

The guard replies, in a feigned, disinterested way:

"They know me better than I know them"; and you can sense him laughing, to himself. "They must be saying that he's a queer old fish." And then he cannot hold back any longer. A smile comes to his mouth.

The young woman breaks into obsequious laughter.

We see another tree pulled down by the force of the Cadagua.

Mud from the last high waters has accumulated on the banks.

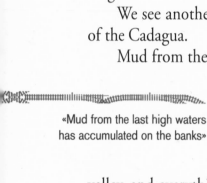

«Mud from the last high waters has accumulated on the banks»

The guard gives us an explanation:

"The river's source is up there, in Burgos. All this is a valley, and everything comes down here. In winter it's very cold here" —his words of explanation end up being directed entirely at her—. "And you're only going as far as Mercadillo. From Valmaseda onwards, and from Bercedo onwards, it's even worse."

"I work in Vadalores", says the young woman. "In Mercadillo I'm just getting off."

"Why so far? Isn't there any job in Alonsótegui that takes your fancy?"

"No, it's just that I was working in Bilbao with a family, and I left because they wanted me to live

70

Reflejas en el cada... FRAGUAS

there, and I did not want to. And then they took
me to where they had a brother. And now I'm
working over there. Well, it's just a place to work!"

We've reached Aranguren. Fernando warns
me that it's time to go and see the driver. And the

author says his farewells speedily, with a quick smile. We have to run. But I can still hear Alicia tell the guard:

"And then at eight fifteen I come back on the Ansa bus."

The Ways of the Cadagua

ENEDINO IS WAITING FOR US with half of his small body leaning out of the window.

Before starting up, he pulls on a cable which runs through half the cabin. It's his horn, the warning whistle. We're off. The actual start is not nearly as exciting when experienced from the engine car. The creaking of the irons can be heard behind us,

«The Cadagua valley is like a corridor in the shape of a large standing S »

far away and intermittent, like the sound of someone stuttering.

Enedino is a tidy driver. His blue uniform is immaculate; his face is shaven, and his veined hands are shiny. More than a uniform it seems like an ecclesiastical habit, and more than a cabin, this seems a pulpit. And his slight body seen from within the cabin has all the harmonious appearance of a priest in the pulpit, or, perhaps even, a canary in its cage. Not a single unexpected movement, nor any use of unwanted force. Just like a canary flitting from his

73

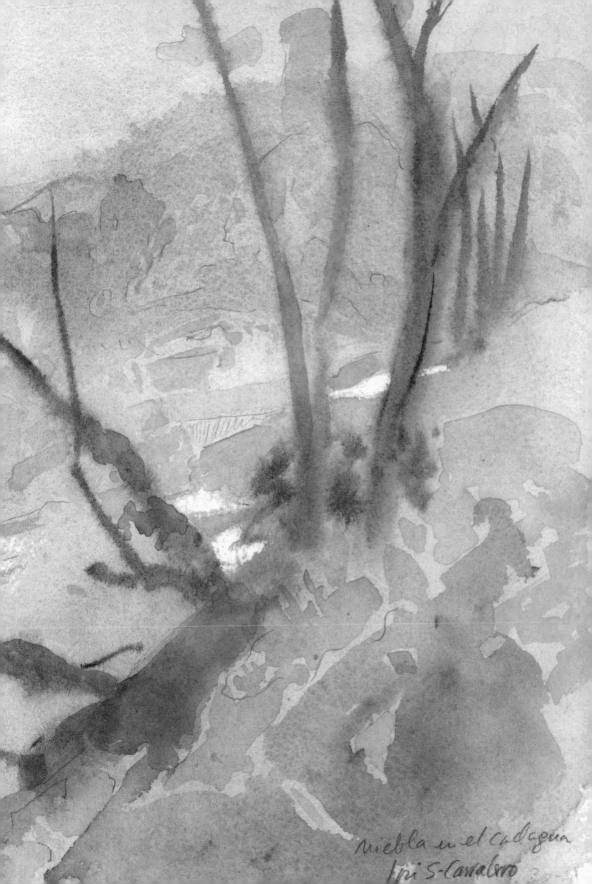

niebla en el cadagua
Ipi S-Caralero

water bowl to his swing, he moves effortlessly from one lever to another.

Enedino is also a circumspect and truly professional driver. Rather than working with pieces of iron, he seems to be handling papers: this one's to be put away, the other's to be kept out… his hands move up and down with great agility, making what is difficult appear easy. Thus it is that the Hullero, in Enedino's hands, slides smoothly along the tracks (how right the Cistierna woman was!) —as smoothly as is possible given the state of the buffers, the irons, the joints, and all this machinery that is as decayed as the Cadagua, along whose valley we are travelling.

The Cadagua valley is like a corridor in the shape of a large standing S that has been pushed slightly forwards, stretching all the way from the Mena Valley in Burgos province right up to the estuary of Bilbao, at Luchana; it is a corridor through which the mistreated Cadagua can observe how the land it has opened up is being fought over by railway lines and villages, roads and factories. It's not for nothing that this valley is the second principal route connecting Vizcaya with the plateaus of Central Spain. The other one, the most important of the two, follows what is called the old Burgos road, along the valley of the Nervión and alongside the Peña de Orduña. That's the route which in medieval times was used to transport all the Castillian and

Leonese wool headed for the ports of Flanders.

However, our route is even more ancient; the discovery of Roman coins in the vicinity of Nervión has made scholars suspect the existence of a Roman road following the Cadagua from the estuary all the way to Castile.

As we leave Aranguren the valley narrows, and —as if the Hullero itself had shaken off all those pestilent urban distractions that make the surroundings of Bilbao so ugly— there now appear tidy, almost coquettish little farms, with cheerful vegetable gardens abundant in beans and apple trees.

The valley gets even narrower as we cross once again the Cadagua on a beautiful metal bridge that magnifies the sounds of the Hullero. Altogether we cross the Cadagua four times.

«We cross once again the Cadagua on a beautiful metal bridge»

Enedino treats us like distinguished guests and, without losing any of the concentration his work requires, takes it upon himself to name everything we see.

"This is the village of La Herrera. This is a factory that makes leaden objects. Look, over there you can see the Cadagua again."

But it's obvious that all the attention we are receiving from Enedino is, for him, merely an additional small burden that comes with his job.

Elder, with its flowers dispersed like little white plates among the foliage, lines the railway bank; a

FRAGUAS

fig tree stands so close to the track that the traveller feels he can almost pull off one of its leaves. Enedino says:

"In Cistierna, as throughout most of Palencia and León, October comes and all the trees lose their foliage. In Cistierna the oaks are only now beginning to open their leaves, but here they have them already."

As we climb up a steep bend, we see to the right a country house with a wooden balustrade, and two red rose beds running along one of the sides of the building. On the other side of the house is a tower built in a golden stone. The tower is small yet solidly built, imposing yet graceful.

For a long while we continue to see the house and its tower, for the Hullero, as it climbs, approaches them as a plane would do a cloud; the plane advances, but the cloud appears to remain the same, absolutely still, and identical in shape, as if the plane was no nearer to it. Thus, from the cabin of the Hullero, we near the house and its tower as from the cockpit of a plane. Nothing seems to move. Perhaps because of this we now see Enedino for what he truly is. Enedino is a pilot, the pilot of a plane that is flying at a height of nine thousand metres.

«The change from steam to diesel took place in the mid sixties»

His diligence, his skill, his efficiency, leads us to think 'what a good vassal he would have been

had he served a worthier lord'. For the Hullero needs an immediate, urgent renovation.

Hazelnut trees fully extend their branches from the side of the railway bank. Further on are some chestnut trees. Every so often little huts can be seen in the middle of fields. Enedino says:

"They're for protecting the farm animals' young offspring."

81

The Hullero now advances across two swollen banks of foliage distinguished by the white and yellow flowers of honeysuckle.

As we get near Valmaseda Enedino repeats the warning he first gave us on leaving Bilbao:

"Remember, this is where the driver changes."

And then, after a pause, he adds:

"But they also change the engine. They're going to put on a yellow one, which is far superior to this."

And it is a fact that this railway, so humble and neglected, has always stood out among Spain's narrow gauge railways for the quantity and power of its engines. During the days of steam travel, it enjoyed the most glorious of heydays, with more that sixty engines using its tracks.

The change from steam to diesel took place in the mid sixties, a date which coincided with the beginning of the railway's decline. Railway buffs might like to know that in 1964 three, French-made, twelve-cylinder Alsthon Electric-Diesel locomotives were acquired; and that in that same year there also came into service five, Belgian-made six-cylinder, Creusot Electric-Diesel locomotives.

And then, in 1965, the acquisition from the North American company General Electric of ten Diesel-electric locomotives made the Hullero once again the envy of its competitors. Until very recently, according to experts, these locomotives were the most powerful ones to have run on Spain's narrow gauge railways, and the ones that truly made this railway's reputation. One of them, our Hullero's true swansong, is the yellow one to which Enedino refers so tenderly.

Valmaseda

T HE RIVER AND THE HULLERO run parallel once again. The river flows downwards, and the Hullero goes up. An acacia truncates the corner of a vegetable garden. The higher branches of some fig trees brush against the railway bank; other figs grow directly above the river. Ivy, with small, oval leaves scalloped at their edges in a light hue, climbs up the poplars along the Cadagua.

«The Ordunte mountains form a straight, bulky profile immediately behind the rooftops of Valmaseda»

The Ordunte mountains form a straight, bulky profile immediately behind the rooftops of Valmaseda, the main town of las Encartaciones. Oaks, chestnuts and arbutus cover their slopes.

These mountains have been more than once the salvation of Valmaseda. On the summit ridge of Mount Kolitza, at a height of 933 metres, can be found the hermitage of San Sebastian, dominating a majestic horizon. The building, partially destroyed during the Civil War, has all the characteristics of

" Iglesia de Valmaseda ..."
por S. Carrales.

the Romanesque, in particular its central door, with its semi-circular arch, which makes the building one of the very few in Vizcaya reminiscent of the magnificent early medieval churches in the Mena Valley. It is solid in construction, with a single nave, and a barrel vault in carved stone. In the stone arch of one of its doors is an inscription recording that 'This was built in 1111'.

There is a local tradition that many inhabitants and families fled to Mount Kolitza to escape the Black Death. It is said that if you look carefully by day you can see the remains of the huts and shacks in which these people lived.

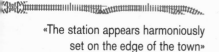

«The station appears harmoniously set on the edge of the town»

The station appears harmoniously set on the edge of the town. The station is one of the architectural joys of the line, with three platforms, a large number of tracks, and a tall, clean building of northern European appearance, with a pitched roof, and fancy brickwork around the windows.

Enedino sets about the ritual of stopping the train with great precision. He whistles. Brakes. Whistles again. Brakes. The Hullero puffs, snorts, sighs like a sperm whale nearing a beach.

Several groups of people are waiting on platform one, to the Hullero's left.

Enedino is going to stay in Valmaseda, and then, after lunch, return to his work. Enedino says again:

"There's now another driver taking over."

He points out to us a a lively group of men, walking down the platform, dressed mainly in blue. Enedino continues:

"He's Basque. He's a tall lad. He's really nice, as you'll see."

The Hullero comes to a halt. Those waiting on the platform approach the train. There's the sound of door handles being opened. Everywhere doors are opening and closing like the flippers of some monstrously sized marine creature desperately searching for oxygen above water. Bags, cases, bundles and packages are being brought in and out. The door of the goods van slams against the fuselage. And all this coming and going, all this raking about in the entrails of the Hullero, comes to seem like the mass activity of some sailing community tearing apart a badly wounded whale stranded on a beach by a storm.

Enedino opens the door to talk to someone who has come up to the engine's left-hand side.

"They're not going to put on the yellow locomotive", says Enedino, clearly upset.

The time has come to say to him our good-byes. We thank him and get off the train together. Enedino tells us:

"Don't mention it. It was a pleasure knowing you". Then he adds:

"Remember, you've just got five minutes. They're not going to change the engine."

We make our way to the centre of the platform. The general hubbub, which is beginning to decrease, is now largely centred on a group of men, almost entirely in blue, who are jovially conversing. The new driver, very tall and corpulent, stands out above the group. Unexpectedly, Enedino sidles up next to us.

"Let me introduce you to the driver", he says, "Hey, Chuchi!"

But he barely succeeds in attracting the attention of this great bulk of a man, so absorbed is the latter in conversation. However, the curiosity shown towards us by the rest of his group make up for the big man's lack of it. Enedino, standing now right beside Chuchi, seems like a launch next to a liner. And then the liner —apparently unintentionally, pushed perhaps simply by the sway of the sea— turns towards the launch. Enedino outlines the reasons for our being here with a concision worthy of that 17th century master of the laconic Gracián, who believed that 'anything that was good was twice as good if said briefly'. And nothing succeeds so quickly or so well as a fulsome allusion to authority. Thus Enedino easily achieves his objective: he makes everyone absolutely aware that we are carrying in our pockets a letter from the director general of the FEVE. And no more need be said.

«The new driver wears his boiler suit like a tower – a blue and gloomy tower»

91

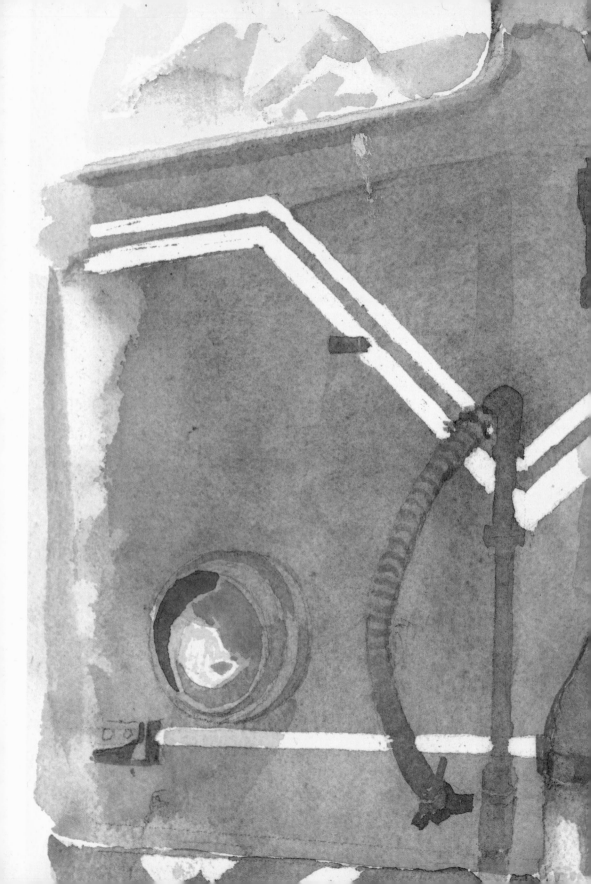

"chuchi el maquinista"
Jri l. Cañales

The new driver (the one to whom the Cilla-mayor woman referred to as the tiger) wears his boiler suit like a tower — a blue and gloomy tower that drops down to the ground from a height of two metres. The tiger of Valmaseda has not the measurements of a tiger but rather those of an elephant. Built like a basketball player, he has shoulders as wide apart as the rails on the track. The author does not remember his first words to this man. Perhaps they were, "We've heard about the yellow locomotive, what a shame". Or perhaps, "This is a wonderful train; we really like it. Let's now see what affect all the recent spending is going to have."

What the author has not forgotten is that whatever he said, he did so with a smile on his face. Nor has he forgotten the driver's reply, spoken with complete seriousness, in a deep and booming voice:

"Oh, fuck all that! The best thing to do would be to put a bloody big bomb under its wheels, and boom!"

We have to go to the goods van to collect a new camera film, and we've got no time to lose. Behind us the group dissolves. Enedino is still following us.

"He's speaks what's on his mind, but he's a good lad."

And he says goodbye again:

"What a shame about the yellow locomotive!"

94

First Impressions
of the Goods Van

T HE AREA AROUND THE GOODS VAN is heaving. The van's interior is narrow, over-used, antiquated. Nonetheless it is like the train's main street: an obligatory stop for travellers withdrawing bags and parcels; a focal point for train workers on duty; a place for a meeting up; or simply an attraction for those walking up and down the station platform.

In the van are two men whom we have already met in Bilbao. When we go in there's a woman on the platform waving farewell.

"And hang the peppers to dry", she says.

"No!", they shout back from inside.

A man immediately behind us breaks into the scene.

"Is there any wine going here?"

"What? You're already after some wine?", says the head of the goods van, handing him over a leather wine gourd.

The man who has asked for the wine has done so without a trace of a smile, as if demanding his rights, or else a favour that is owed him.

When he drinks he does so also very seriously. He stops having a swig, and gives back the gourd, and goes off as gravely and disdainfully as he had come.

The head of the goods van silently puts back the gourd in its place. He's a tall man with dark and expressive eyes, the eyes of someone whom experience has made very understanding of others. He asks us why we're doing the journey. After his thirty-two years of service, he still believes that improvements on the line are just about to come.

"It looks now as if an investment of 11,000 million pesetas over the next six to eight years is coming".

This 'coming' business is something we've heard countless times since childhood. The monarchy is coming, the Americans are coming, the end of the world is coming. It is as if all that is coming, if it is coming, is coming despite ourselves, without our willing it, whether we like it or not.

The head of the goods van is called Nazario Rodríguez Vergara. He's from León, and, as he says, lives in León itself, meaning the capital of the province. Though into his fifties, he still keeps his exuberant and almost completely black hair.

"I've been doing this now for twenty years, and, up to seven years ago, we used to have to carry about three thousand tons of coal daily from León. Now we only have to carry from eight hundred to a thousand tons of sand. From Arija".

Oslé enters the van. He comes straight up to us.

"Two employees of the railway have got on to the train and occupied your seats. As the two of you never stop moving around for a minute I've said that that was okay."

At first we don't understand. Oslé explains himself again:

"The pressure's finally on. And as you two are all over the place, I said it didn't matter."

We agree. and then Oslé reaffirms what's been said:

"Exactly! Just what I told them: as these two are reporters, there'll be no problem."

Then he goes up to Nazario:

"The back coach is going to stay in Espinosa. The inspector says so."

We ask him why

"Because there's no need of it. It'll just be travelling empty."

It's now all clear on either side of the Hullero. The engine whistles. Everything's back to as it was. The starting up is achieved with a triple rhythm, that's to say three jerks or three convulsions. Plum, plum, plum, or zas, zas, zas. There's no more to say on the matter.

"Okay, now that I'm here", says Oslé to Nazario, "sign this piece of paper."

We look through the right-side window, with our backs turned to the station's principal building. We are offered a view of the old part of town, which comprises four long streets truncated, Manhattan-style, by three short ones. Diminutive, medieval, and set among mountains, this most unlikely of Manhattans is crossed by the Cadagua, which meanders around its old houses like some spoilt lord, blasé of emblems and coats of arms.

Between the river and the tracks runs a quiet promenade shaded by umbrellas-shaped trees. Our old driver, Enedino, is walking along it, at a good pace, and in the direction of the train. When he sees us he waves goodbye to us.

"Enedino!", we shout, returning his gesture.

"Enedino Llamazares", pedantically echoes the monotonous voice behind us of Oslé.

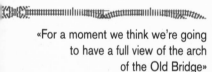

«For a moment we think we're going to have a full view of the arch of the Old Bridge»

For a moment we think we're going to have a full view of the arch of the Old Bridge, a structure as ancient and beautiful —if not more so— than the famous one of Cangas de Onís.

As the rattling of the Hullero against the rails increases, the author is overcome with a nostalgia for what now can never be. This note-taking traveller would have liked to have stopped in Valmaseda, walk through its streets, go up to the Cadagua, and, from the parapet of its bridge, let a pebble drop straight into its waters. For the very oldness of the town, and the way in which the Cadagua —and the Hu-

El puente que no río Aparicio

y el puente

Iril-Carralero

llero, and the many tracks that converge here— have taken over the role of the now distant sea, and, subtly conferred on the whole a distinctively maritime air, give to the place a pleasingly simple and immediate character: the character of a noble refuge, of a refuge for mariners lost on a mountainous shore.

Nazario enhances our disappointment:

"The FEVE has a railway yard here, The Valmaseda Rail Works, and you can no longer see the bridge."

With the exception of the driver, all those working on the Hullero are travelling with us now in the goods van: Luis García Oslé, the guard; Nazario Rodríguez Vergara, the head of the goods van; and Sergio Álvarez, the man from Mataporquera, the one who —when accompanied by the stationmaster— had made us feel in Concordia we were inspecting the coaches.

The material in the railway yard is arranged in a large semi-circle, on the inner side of which are dark holes like burrows, caves for iron dragons, places for the resting and treating, transplanting and repairing, of bits of steel and wrought iron, axle boxes and nuts.

A skinny railway worker, wearing a Basque beret, and a baggy boiler suit like that of a sailor, stands in the middle of the semi-circle like a haughty matador in a bull ring. Arms akimbo, his back to the dark boards, he watches the Hullero pass by.

100

The whole rail yard has a unifying filth. The earth over which the tracks run, the crumbling walls and roofs, everything has the same ash-coloured, ancient, and dusty look. The heyday of the yards seems to belong to the distant past.

"Who owned this before?"

"Robla", is Oslé's laconic reply.

We are recommended to enjoy the climb up the Mena Valley from the driver's cab.

But because we're still in the goods van, Nazario, the boss here, is the one who has taken upon himself the role of guide.

"This is La Pinilla. Slightly further on is Burgos", he says.

"Further on there's a house of a brother of mine who lived around here", says Oslé.

«The FEVE has a railway yard here, The Valmaseda Rail Works»

"A bit further on is a beret factory", says Nazario,

"La Encartada", says Oslé, then adding: "From this point we're already in Burgos. This is where the lines from Burgos, Vizcaya and Vitoria all meet up."

Nazario does not give up:

"Further up's a reservoir, the Ordunte, which supplies Bilbao with all its water."

We crowd in turn around the window, with the author literally squashed against the door, which he thinks is one that is likely to open outwards. Oslé confirms this to be the case:

"It'as all so cramped in here that if were to open inwards… well, for start, there's this safe here", he says, pointing to an enormous, black metal safe, "…the whole place would be like a bloody loom".

"What's in the safe? Anything of value?"

"Cash".

I ask them if in all their years of travelling nothing unusual has ever happened to them.

"Here? Not once! Not once!", says Nazario.

"Not once! Not once!", corroborates Sergio Álvarez.

"Not even any accident?"

"Well, accidents, of course", says Oslé, "but nothing fatal, nothing like that happens here. Not like when I was in Villaverde, about twenty years ago, and a woman threw herself off the bridge over the Almuhey."

«At the Station of Arla-Berrón we get off the goods van, and rush towards the locomotive»

I lean my notebook against the large metal safe, so that I can take down the address of Nazario, to whom we have promised to send some of Fernando's photos. The jolting of the train makes my hand fall on top of the paper. Oslé says:

"There's no need to lean. You've got to stand up, and, look, do this: using these muscles here at the back of your legs, flex your knees, and support them from behind with one of your hands."

The Cadagua continues flowing to the right. We

Castelo en Arla Berm
FRANAS.

are approaching its source. The water is now flowing clean, and, for the first time, you can see the
white edges of its bed. Ivy is spreading over the trunks
of a multitude of poplars.

At the Station of Arla-Berrón we get off the goods van, and rush towards the locomotive. The engine is raging.

"Chuchi! Oy, Chuchi!", we shout, "let us in!"

"Come on, get in!"

The Tiger of Valmaseda

W<small>E ENTER</small> by the left-hand door, where Chuchi is to be found at the controls, and cross over to the other side of the engine car. To the train's left can still be seen the station building; to the right, almost at the level of our eyes, a young woman is bent over a strip of arable land that intrudes on the slope of the railway bank.

«The sky, in which cumulus clouds are gathering, has a more distant horizon»

There's something in the atmosphere that indicates we are about to climb. The sky, in which cumulus clouds are gathering, has a more distant horizon, and the dark peaks are scattered more loosely along this greenest of valleys.

Chuchi says all of a sudden:

"Good morning, eh?" —and that "eh?" seems to contain a warning.

"Good morning", we reply in unison as in the chorus of a musical.

"You're going to León then?", I ask him.

"Yes. We're going to León."

Whereas Enedino adapted himself perfectly to the proportions of the driver's cabin, the gigantic Chuchi is all disproportions, disharmony. Chuchi looks squeezed, sandwiched into the space, like the chained Sigismund in Calderón de la Barca's famous play *Life is a Dream*, whose every movement forces him against the walls of his cell.

"I imagine you're looking forward to this all being over", I tell him.

"Of course, after forty three years of doing this!", he exclaims, throwing his head backwards.

"Forty-three years here, on this railway?"

"Forty-three years, eh? Without stopping, eh? And I was in the war too. Corporal in artillery in the Navarre 4th Division. I'll be sixty on the first of October."

«Dozens of cows, mainly white, are grazing in the meadows»

"But in the war, were you also working for the railways?"

"No, before, before, eh?"

"So you mean you weren't with the railway in the war?"

"Noo!", he says, before adding after a brief pause, and with unexpected meekness: "But my war service helped me a lot, it did."

"In terms of your job?"

"I, as I was with Franco, it helped me a lot."

Outside, dozens of cows, mainly white, are grazing in the meadows.

"I was also with the Reds, I was."

"Oh, yes."

"I was with them, yes. With the Reds and the Nationalists. With the two of them."

"But you finished up with the Nationalists."

"More like they finished us, which is not quite the same!", he exclaims, letting out a short and ambiguous laugh.

The Hullero is now travelling right in the middle of the broad valley, without the habitual presence of the Cadagua at its side.

"You'll see it again later", says Chuchi.

Chuchi is driving standing up, with his enormous body bent of necessity over the controls. His feet are wide apart, with his left hand controlling a lever, and the other resting on the metal instruments panel, a piece of steel wool constantly in his grip.

The harsh roar of the engine is a serious obstacle to conversation.

"I'm carrying the stew in here", says Chuchi, pointing to the floor, where we see, between his legs, a metal tripod supporting a pot.

"I had one hell of a chorizo in there!", he says, "but I gave it to the fat man, because I don't want to eat so much. All I've got now are two chops, nothing else."

To give some idea of this chorizo's dimensions, he straightens his left hand, extends the index finger as much as it will go, and uses the index finger on the other hand to draw a line all the way to the forearm.

Chuchi bends over to take the lid off the pot. He stares inside with almost a look of ecstasy on his face, and says again:

"I had a chorizo this size… and I gave it away. I don't want to eat so much."

"And you intend to eat like this, as we go along?"

"Of course!"

"And where will you eat."

"When I get hungry. Further on, at the source of the Ebro, in the province of Santander."

The Hullero runs now through a more open space, where two tributaries of the Cadagua, the Ordunte and the Romario, flow towards each other, on either side of the train, eventually to deposit their waters in El Berrón. Hillocks and hills make the land gently uneven. Beyond, on the far right, rises the range of the Ordunte, while, in front of us, are the distant, foreshortened walls of rock of the Peña Losa.

We are stepping into the atrium of that first kingdom of Castile, the Castile that came and went, and which, for some people, contains the Basque and Cantabrian soul.

More than fifty cows are resting on the green hillside that is sliced by the railway bank. Some of them get up, not frightened, but quickly, and stare completely absorbed as each coach of the Hullero goes by. Their whiteness (as white as their very milk, as those clouds that are searching a way out of the valley), their pink noses, and their peaceful serenity —all this inspires in the spectator a sense of elation. Chuchi says:

"I live in Espinosa because I like it more than Valmaseda; because it's healthier, and there's more cattle."

I see for the first time the red rose that Chuchi tucks behind his ear.

"Do you always go around with that flower on your ear?"

He makes an imprecise gesture.

"Two flowers?"

"No. Just one. One flower."

"What flower is that?"

"I always tell everyone as a joke that they're talismans, and they're El Viti's."

"What?"

"Talismans, of El Viti, you know, the bullfighter! I tell them we're related."

"So you tuck it behind your ear and keep it on for the whole journey? Every day?"

"And I add another when I'm in León!"

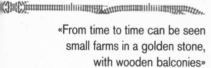

From time to time can be seen small farms in a golden stone, with wooden balconies, and climbing roses framing their doors. They are usually surrounded by vegetable gardens, or agricultural fields, which give the impression that the farm buildings themselves are just another product of the earth.

We are beginning to descend. The Hullero puffs. It seems to suffer as much when restrained as when it is forced to climb. It snorts. It complains.

So does Chuchi:

"They should have used those thingamajigs here."

But it's difficult to hear him. His voice, a barely modulated gust of wind, is confused at times with the hoarse snoring of the engine.

"What?", I shout.

Chuchi repeats himself:

"They should have used here those thingamajigs,

UNGO-NAVA
FRAGUAS.

thingamajigs... you know, those German things. This engine is French. Made in Laval."

While the Hullero descends, Chuchi rubs the steel wool against the joins of the instrument panel. He does this like a rider stroking the neck of his mount.

We are searching for the Cadagua, our old and now beautiful friend. But it's not there. Chuchi points out to our right a dark and distant hillside down which, according to him, the river Ordunte descends through pines.

"But what about the Cadagua?"

"The Cadagua? Oh, you'll see it, don't worry!", answers Chuchi.

Four large brick warehouses with white roofs extend over one of the small natural amphitheatres into which the valley is broken up.

«The Hullero continues braking, puffing, suffering. We cross a level crossing»

"It's the wood factory", says Chuchi.

Bushes of elder, swollen and sparse, dotted with white flowers, grow on both sides of the railway bank.

"There's the reservoir", says Chuchi. But it is difficult to make out anything on the dark hillside. "The dam is forty metres high, bigger than that of the Ebro. But the Ebro dam is more striking because it's right in the mountains."

The Hullero continues braking, puffing, suffering. We cross a level crossing, and Chuchi tells us:

"That's the main road!"

Towards Peña Losa

UNGO-NAVA. From this station, situated at the lowest point of the Mena Valley, it's all uphill. The Mena has two powerful guardians: the Sierra de Ordunte to the north; the mountains of La Peña to the south. The easiest entrance into the valley is from the northeast, going through the narrow gap cut into El Berrón by the Cadagua —the route chosen by the Hullero as it heads towards León.

The valley of the Mena covers an area of fifty-nine square kilometers, in which few more than five thousand people live, and is governed by a single municipality, Villasana, which is spread out over farmsteads and neighbourhoods numbering about fifty.

Chuchi says:

"Do you know where I was recently? Do you know where? …Where they buried… whatshisname… that television man… the one who made nature programmes… Rodríguez de la Fuente."

"Really?"

119

"His father's there as well."

"Buried there?"

But Chuchi does not answer. He simply says:

"We're going to see the Cadagua over there. It passes over here. It comes from over there. And now goes over there."

We begin the climb. The engine roars. The whole Hullero shakes. Chuchi rubs his huge hand over the engine's back, as he wipes off the motor's sweat with his steel wool.

"And can't you sit down here?", I ask him.

"Yes. Here's a seat", he says, turning around to open a folding seat which slams shut the moment he lets go of it. "I don't much care for sitting down when I'm on the move".

«It's difficult to recognixe the Cadagua now that it's so brilliant and clean»

"I thought", I tell him, "that a train always has two drivers. Why aren't there two?"

"They had to go!"

"Why?"

"Don't know. With so much unemployment today!"

Chuchi continues talking, but his deep voice fails to rise over the desperate din of the motor.

"There's the Cadagua!" he then exclaims.

We don't see it.

"There, there, in between the poplars!"

But it's difficult to recognize our old friend

El Cadafua "aseada"
FRAGUAS.

now that it's so brilliant and clean; now that we are heading towards its source. It's to the right of us, a few metres below, fringed by its faithful companions —those ivy-ringed poplars that accompany it all the way to the Nervión, turning it into a shy river which hides and winds its way in the shadows like a mole.

We continue climbing. The valley is now at its most open. In front of us, though still very distant, rises a tall, elongated mountain, a concave wall crenellated with grey rocks. It is the Peña Losa, a range which shows us now its most forbidding side, its high cliffs resembling an agitated wave about to crash down on the valley.

The Hullero, unperturbed, continues towards this mountainous mass. The train's noise is deafening. It whistles.

"Don't you see the water?", says Chuchi.

But the great din dulls the senses, slows your reactions.

"There it is! Yes, there it is!"

Chuchi pulls the cord and the Hullero whistles. Once, twice.

The noise of the engine is so great that it encourages you to retreat into yourself. Chuchi leans towards the cooking pot, lifts up its lid, and stares at the dark, bubbling contents.

The halt stop of Menamayor is to the left. The building is almost like a mountain refuge. A rose bush grows thickly above the door, framing it with red roses the size of apples.

The man in charge, an elderly man, sits in shirt sleeves on a deck chair, watching the railway bank as if this were a river and he a placid fisherman.

The Hullero does not stop, and the man gets up quickly, smiles, and makes a curious gesture, clearly for the benefit of Chuchi. He lifts up his arms and half extends them as if he were dancing. Or rather as if he were in a bullfight about to place his banderillas.

The Hullero emits a long whistle, and Chuchi makes a routine gesture of greeting.

Cows take over the playful fields of the the Mena Valley. Some are grayish brown, but most are white, white with black patches. They seem the true owners of the valley, the ones who most enjoy it. Those nearest to the track display only mild surprise as they are forced to their feet by the approach of the train.

«We pass near a tiny cemetery with white and grey, peeling walls»

The Hullero continues its brave advance towards the Peña Losa. According to Chuchi, rather than the speedometer (which does not work), we are climbing at a speed of thirty-five kilometers per hour.

We pass near a tiny cemetery with white and grey, peeling walls. It seems an abandoned garden to which has clustered an unruly grove of dark cypresses.

...parece un jardín abandonado.
José S-Carralero.

The valley has so much beauty, and Spring here is clearly so gentle and agreeable, that the idea of being buried in this tiny cemetery seems an especially attractive way of preparing to return to paradise. Everywhere grow oaks, walnut trees, chestnuts, and fruit trees. Playful tapestries, in every hue of green, soften the outline of hillocks, hills, and mountains.

The Hullero advances with relentless tenacity. Chuchi strokes the engine's back with his steel wo-ol, which he also rubs, from time to time, against his hands.

"What do you use it for, to clean yourself with?", I ask him.

"As a rag, I've got loads of them", he says, pointing to the plastic bags that cover the instruments panel.

«The water tower has a square basin that is supported by four iron legs»

We reach Mercadillo-Vi-llasana, where Alicia gets off. Fernando and I lean out of the window. The water tower has a square basin that is supported by four iron legs. Through them we can see part of the station, which, like all the others in the valley, is isolated, and far from the villages which it serves.

The station is built into the hillside, and is reached by cars along a rough dirt track. The building has two floors, the first one being wider than the second, which rises above it like a central tower.

Alicia takes her time in getting down. We wave

to her, but she does not look at us. Instead she stands with her back to us, lifting her hand in the air by way of saying goodbye. Then she gets into a blue Renault 5, driven by a young man.

Suddenly the Hullero goes backwards. Chuchi stops it, then says to us:

"Somebody's pulled the vacuum brake".

A man in shirt sleeves with a jacket bundled up under his arm approaches the engine car. He arrives laughing. He bends down in front of the Hullero and pulls up a few poppies that are growing on the side of the tracks. Then he lifts them up to his ear. He walks up to Chuchi, making fun of him. He seems to be saying, "Tuck the flower under your ear, or else everything will go badly."

Chuchi doesn't turn a hair. He dismisses him with a wave of the hand, and asks:

"Have we been given permission to go?"

We then turn towards the station master, who is next to us, and, who raises his flag that very instant. We head off.

Chuchi says immediately:

"That road you see over there is the one that goes to Amurrio."

Navigating the Heights

Now that we are crossing the Mena Valley, we can truly appreciate the achievement of the man responsible for building the line—the industrial engineer José Manuel Oraá. When commemorating him in 1948 the Railway Company—without in any way diminishing the man's aesthetic sensibility—singled out sturdiness and thrift as the two main qualities guiding the project. How true this is! The Hullero hugs the ground like a true beast of the mountains, a mythological centipede. Without major building works, or long tunnels, or excessive leveling of the ground, the train follows the landscapes' contours with an almost innate strength, as if instead of buffers and chains it was made of bones and a soul.

This is perhaps why the man who executed the line made the gradients no steeper than one in five, limited the minimum curve radius to 120 metres, and established a track weight of 23.5 kg (only later was this substituted for the present 45 kg).

No great mountains had to be opened up to allow the Hullero to pass. For the whole of the train's 340 kilometre journey, it has to go through only twenty-one tunnels (the longest of which is barely a kilometer in length), and cross twenty relatively unimportant bridges, the largest of which, at ninety metres long, is the metal one across the Ebro.

"This is Villasana", says Chuchi. And there is the valley's capital, this cluster of noble, white painted houses directly in between the Sierra de Ordunte and the mountains of la Peña, the valley's two massively sized guardians.

We have reached the great wall of the Peña Losa, and are now moving around its lap, like a drop of water slithering in the palm of one's hand.

There's honeysuckle on both sides of the railway bank, great bushes of honeysuckle, covered in flowers. And there are also elder flowers and ferns.

From the engine car you see the landscape once again as if from the cockpit of a plane, or from the prow of a ship; for it as if the Hullero is floating, and the surrounding ground shifting, almost as if the engine, as it advances, is throwing up a spray of broom, honeysuckle and hawthorn.

The noise of the motor is the only disturbing feature. Chuchi lifts up once more the lid of his pot, to uncover again his stew. Deaf to all the noise, he says:

"I had a chorizo like this", using the same gesture

as before to make us aware of the chorizo's exceptional proportions.

The beauty of the climb is holding us spellbound. We continue making our way through the Peña Losa, along the curve of its lap. Large and mysterious beech woods climb its near vertical escarpments. Chuchi says:

"There are good mushrooms here."

You can see as well oaks and cypresses, and a few pines with strange, dark crests. Hazelnut tress alternate with the honeysuckle.

Anzo, a cluster of white houses, is to our left. Herds of white and grayish brown cows dot the slopes.

"There's a lot of cattle around here", comments Chuchi.

«A few rooks, four or six, encircle the engine like horseflies on the back of an ox»

We are now deep in the Peña's fold, and aiming directly towards the range's front wall, towards the very centre of its curvature; it is as if the train had decided to go right inside the mountain. A few rooks, four or six, encircle the engine like horseflies on the back of an ox. Most of the mountain is shrouded in a dark green blanket, which only gives out towards the summit, in a ravine-scarred cliff which runs the whole length of the ridge like an architectural border.

We pull up at the halt stop of Anzo, now to our right. Chuchi asks once more:

"... los grajos remotábanos ..."
Luis Cernalou.

"Have we got the go-ahead, to leave?"

We continue. Honeysuckle swells the borders of the railway bank. Ferns spread out beyond the woods. These are lands barely frequented by man. The Hullero crosses them in an almost surreptitious fashion. The Hullero is an ecological train.

Chuchi tells us that he once killed a wild boar here.

"It was a boar weighing thirty kilos. A young female. The engine hit her, and broke her hip. We went out with this iron rod, this one here, and gave it to her on the neck. And that was that. Thirty kilos, she weighed. About four or five years ago."

«Ferns spread out beyond the woods»

The Peña is crowned by a cloud, a white, compact, greybellied cloud, which has attached itself to one of the summit's crags. The cliff is grey and sharp like the blade of a knife.

"That is La Valca, the photo factory", says Chuchi. And he points to a group of large, clean warehouses rising alone above the rolling green valley.

On the opposite side, to our left, a donkey —a true *Platero*, stubborn and hairy, silvery grey, short in height, a straw doll for tourists— lops off part of a wooden fence, in a field full of cows. There would be something almost archaic about its presence were it not for the train, or this valley, whose earth is arranged in gentle, rounded hollows as if better to

134

"Helecho"
FRAGNAS.

accommodate the movements of man. Chuchi says:

"They use donkeys here to carry things: rubbish, grass."

And its thick, sheep-like coat, so appropriate to a peace-loving creature, brings to mind a completely different type of beast:

"It's a long time since bears have been seen here. They're disappearing."

The railway bank ploughs through a wild garden, whose lush greenness is speckled with reds, whites and yellows. There are hawthorn flowers, resembling large and fleshy daisies.

We reach Vigo-Siones. It's ten past eleven; we're twenty-five minutes behind schedule, after two and a half hours of travelling.

The morning is effervescent. The clouds push each other, gather together, scatter, and open up to reveal patches of blue sky; from time to time bursts through a diagonal ray of sunshine, resembling a ramp down which the dampness can descend.

I ask Chuchi to name all the instruments on the panel. The noise muffles much of what he says, and even drowns the intermittent sounds of the wheels. Chuchi says:

"This is to change speed, these are the gears, to go forward, to go backwards. And this is the over-feed", indicating with the appropriate hand what each thing is for. "And this is the fuel indi… And this is for using the traction motors. And this is to charge the batteries. And this is the pressure gauge... And this is to put on the train's lights. And this is the train's vacuum brake. And this is the engine's vacuum brake."

This is, and this is, and this is. Thus is the way of talking of someone to whom the first will always come last, for the only instrument he has used consistently from the very beginning, and which he never lets go of, is precisely the last one to which he points.

THE MENA VALLEY

W E HAVE GAINED HEIGHT. We are perched in the middle of La Peña, and have a bird's eye view of the valley.

From the north the Mountains of Orduña roll down gently towards the valley, in a series of wooded slopes, hills, and hillocks that come to an end by the windy shores of a now pure and bucolic Cadagua.

«We are perched in the middle of La Peña, and have a bird's eye view of the valley»

This valley of marvels that is the Mena is a hidden treasure amidst the rough, dry expanses of Castile. You rarely read about it. Even Dionisio Ridruejo, such a devotee of this mountainous, northern Castile —this Castile of Basque appearance, damp and discreet— barely mentions it.

What he does say is that this is wonderful country, that the Cadagua flows into the North Sea; that the place names are heavily Basque; that there are some Romanesque churches in a golden stone (such as

"Valle del Mena
Jois S. Carralew

that of Vallejo, with its curious apse), and a few towers in this style (the impressively tall one of Lezama, for instance); that there remain several of the more than five hundred hermitages that were once in the valley; and that the houses have sun-traps and widely projecting eaves.

The author, who hates all the crimes committed against nature in the name of development, is happy that the Mena Valley remains as it is. However, he thinks that if Spain were a less uncouth place, the route he is following would be one of the most important tourist attractions in the country; that the Hullero would be one of Spain's major tourist trains. In this valley you will find archaeological remains, historical relics, unique landscapes, vistas only possible from the Hullero, places that are integral to this country's origins, and which have remained exactly as they were more than a thousand years ago, when they were subject to the violent raids of the Muwallad Muza, 'the third king of Spain'. Or even as they were two thousand years ago when a ray of lightening killed one of the slaves who was carrying across these woods the litter of Augustus, the conqueror of Cantabria.

The English have turned many of their narrow gauge railways into tourist attractions, and have maintained in the process several of the old steam trains. In Wales alone there are eight narrow gauge railways, all working on steam, and all helping towards a greater knowledge of the country. The French have created Cénevol, the ultimate in tourist trains, which goes from Paris to Marseilles by way of Clermont-Ferrand, going around volcanoes, skirting the banks of rivers through a *'pays rude, pays fier, pays des anciens camisards.'* (Just think, what could be said about the lands through which the Hullero travels). A stewardess hands out to each traveller on the Cénevol a leaflet featuring the train's itinerary, the notable monuments, and all the points of interest to be seen in the course of the journey, together with full historical and geographical information.

But perhaps all this would be too much for the modest Hullero, perhaps it wouldn't be able to bear all this.

The Hullero whistles and puffs and until it comes almost to a dead halt.

"We've got to go through two tunnels here", says Chuchi.

He puts his hand on a round indicator and says:

"And this is the mileometre, which doesn't work".

When he touches one of the controls with his huge hands, he does so in such a way that the ironwork must feel as protected as a patient does when a poultice is applied to his chest.

"What are you going to do when you retire?"

Chuchi doesn't hesitate for a moment.

"I'll be walking around, here and there!"

"Really?"

Yes. Chuchi is absolutely sure.

"I'll be here one day, and the next over there. Off to see the cattle!"

"Where will you go and live?"

"I'll stay in Espinosa".

The tunnel makes us go quiet. And before entering the next one, I ask him if he still remembers the steam engines.

"They were tough, they were, I know they were", he says, but without, apparently, any of the sense of release that nostalgia usually induces. "There were one hundred engines". Then he adds spitefully, "And they sold the bloody lot of them. They didn't leave a single bloody one... And there were some engines from Algeria; I remember one of them...It was really strong, it was, you could tell... the wheels were as tall as I was... Before coming here, the train used to carry forty-five thousand litres of water through the African desert, through Algeria, even got as far as the territory of Addis Abeba."

«The tunnel makes us go quiet...»

"What speed could the engines reach?"

"They were no faster than these. But they carried more cargo than now. Their coal car was half the size of one of these engines."

We pass by the halt stop of Cadagua at eleven sixteen, and immediately enter another tunnel. The noise

"...El tunel nos hace callar..."

Luis Caballer.

Valle de Mena
desde el apeadero de CABAÑA
FRAGUAS.

is battering us. Chuchi wipes away all the grease that the train exudes. And he complains:

"This is really dirty, this is. These locomotives aren't good."

Inside the tunnel everything is the colour of coal, just like looking down a mine shaft. But suddenly we emerge into a resplendent green.

"The village down there is Cadagua", says Chuchi.

The village of Cadagua, more than one hundred metres below us, stretches out below the Peña Losa like a handful of white clothes scattered in the green grass beneath a wall.

"That's the source of the Cadagua", says Chuchi.

We make an effort to look for it.

«The village of Cadagua stretches out below the Peña Losa like a handful of white clothes scattered in the green grass»

"Down there. Don't you see it? Don't you see it? It's a bad river. It often gets furious."

We raise our eyes a few metres above the houses, to the foot of the escarpment on which our train is perched. We hope to find a small, bubbling white spring whose waters grow as others join them. But no. The Cadagua is a river without a childhood. It is born as a fully formed adult, like a great gash at the foot of the mountain.

Chuchi says:

"Over towards Cornejo, on the other side of the mountains, there's a river that disappears underground. Some say that this is the one that comes out here."

148

The Hullero continues climbing, and on reaching —just above Lezama— a corner of the mountain where the valley seems finally to come to an end, the panorama is even broader than before. You can see the valley's capital of Villasana, the "Healthy Town" (what an appropriate name!), which we thought we had left behind a long while before. You can see the Mena's smaller communities, shining like patches of snow above the valley. You can see the two main roads which head north. "The Ansa buses always come past here", says Chuchi. You can see how the roads join the Cadagua at Villasana as if they were tributaries of the river. More memorably, you can see La Peña's unusual curved escarpment, which is like a cross between the Great Wall of China, and an agitated wave that has been petrified on the point of breaking over the valley. And, finally, you can see the Hullero, contorting itself as it follows the mountain's curve. From the engine car, we observe its brown, old body as it twists its way above the great valley like a toy train, like a silk worm suspended from a lettuce leaf.

BERCEDO, STEW AND ROAD

THE HULLERO DOES NOT STOP at Cantonad. Chuchi says mysteriously:

"The hermitage here contains the shoulder of Saint Michael."

The broom seems to jump up as the train passes, scattering itself into mounds over the slopes and banks.

Chuchi hardly speaks. Next to the track are some other rails that have been dismantled. I ask him what this is all about.

"They've taken them off because they're already old".

"So the track we're on is new?"

"Oh no! It seems new until it falls apart."

Chuchi is silent again. He lifts the lid off his cooking pot. This gesture seems to isolate him from his surroundings.

"What did you say you call this?", I ask.

He is surprised.

"This? The pot! All my life I've called it a bloody pot. A pot's a pot."

"Is it aluminium?"

"What, the pot? Of course."

"Does the same charcoal last the whole time?"

"No. I've got some more, and I throw it on when needed", he says, pointing to the numerous plastic bags, small, medium and large that lie scattered over the metal instrument panel.

Chuchi shuts up once more, and looks again at his pot. When he lifts up his head, he sees the main road:

"Look, over there, there's the main road!"

Then he adds:

"Look, there's a lorry!"

"This road, where does it go, to Burgos?"

"To Burgos, to Palencia, to León, to just about everywhere. Even to Santander."

The author is sure that Chuchi, were it possible, would have already driven the locomotive over onto the asphalt, to free himself from the burden of tracks, to avoid being a slave to time-tables. For Chuchi clearly likes roads, and likes naming the places to where they are going. Nothing about the landscape —neither the woods, nor the rivers, nor the mountains (well, perhaps, the cattle)— is capable of moving him so much as does the sight of roads.

To the right, closing off the Mena Valley, are a few strange clearings on the hills crossed by the main road; they seem to be signs to be read from above, hieroglyphic-like glades inscribed into the main hillside.

"You can see the reservoir!", says Chuchi.

"What reservoir?"

"That of the Ordunte."

On the other side of the valley we can make out the white concrete walls of the dam, looking almost like a belvedere.

Chuchi takes another glance inside his pot. In doing so he seems to enclose himself within an imaginary room that extends from his inclined head to his open legs. While in this position, watching his bubbling stew, he appears to be meditating.

The author is reluctant to interrupt him in these moments of intimacy; but he does so none the less.

«On the other side of the valley we can make out the white concrete walls of the dam, looking almost like a belvedere»

"What have you got in there? Can I have a look?"

And I crouch down within his private space. In the pot are stewing peppers, potatoes, a few chunks of meat. Chuchi says.

"The chorizo was this big", and he makes again that now all too familiar gesture, with his left index finger extended, and the right one resting on his left fore-arm. "I gave it to a fat man who came into the engine car. It was home-made, really good. This big it was."

We are leaving the valley, but such is the Mena's

"pantano do Ordunte."
José S. Cavaleri.

magical hold that the Hullero has to gain momentum before being able to leave. This is why the train's route up the Peña Losa has traced the curve of a tautened catapult about to release its projectile.

We are now facing another valley. Old rails continue to be stacked up parallel to the track. The green leaves of beeches glisten on the hillsides. The hazelnut trees, pale and shy, sway in between the hawthorn and the heather.

The Hullero whistles. The main road comes into view. We go towards it. At the end of a straight stretch of line is a level crossing. A flag is raised by a signalman, who turns out to be a woman. She greets Chuchi. The Hullero whistles. Chuchi says:

«The Hullero stops at the station of Bercedo-Montija»

"That's the main road".

The landscape has changed. We are higher. The Peña Losa has shaken loose the Hullero, and has set it off on its way towards the other valleys of northern Castile. The woodland is scarcer, and there are occasional stone walls marking out the properties. In the distance rises what seems like another mountain range broken up into five enormous ridges. These are the peaks of Bedón, Picón, Las Vallejeras, Oricedo, and Cornejo. They look like a group of giant pyramids that have lined up next to each other to watch the Hullero go by.

We cross a bridge.

156

Estación de Bercedo
FRAGUAS.

"This river has a Basque name: I think it's the Cerneja. It leads to the Ordunte", says Chuchi.

The Hullero stops at the station of Bercedo-Montija. The Basque mountaineer Néstor de Goicoechea recommends coming to this station to begin the climb up to the Zalama which, at 1,3412 metres, is the highest peak of the Ordunte range. The impression Goicoechea gives is that the climb up to the top is little more than a stroll. He says you have to take the Lanestosa road until you reach the

"Las cinco masas"
Jou S-Carraleo

village of Aguera, from where you continue until the outskirts of San Pelayo, where you will find, to the left of the road, a path running along the top of a small plateau. Soon you will come to a boundary stone which is where four municipalities and three provinces come together: the Soba Valley, which belongs to Santander; the former territory of Montijo and the Mena Valley, both of which are in Burgos; and the Carranza Valley, which forms part of Vizcaya.

The view from the top of the Zalama is apparently magnificent. Goicoechea writes that 'The panorama over the valleys and territories marked out by the boundary stone is truly marvelous, with the horizons bordered by long rows of mountains, and by the wild, blue expanse of the Cantabrian sea.'

«In the distance rises what seems like another mountain range broken up into five enormous ridges»

We decide to go back into the coachess. Surprisingly, Chuchi is enormously disappointed by this:

"You mean, you're going back there?"

We say yes, to which he replies, in an almost imploring and uncharacteristically pained tone:

"Then you'll have to come here again".

"How much time do we stop here?", we ask him, all prepared to run.

But Chuchi says quite adamantly:

"No need to run. Take your time."

ESPINOSA OF THE RICH

W E GET INTO A SECOND CLASS COACH which occupies one of the third class carriages of old. It's almost midday and, after our little run, are suddenly tired for the first time on the journey. We enter the coach with every intention of sitting down. The coach is all noise, just like some gathering of friends. The passengers look at us; those nearest the aisle either repeat the last word they've been saying as we pass by, or else pause to search for a way of expressing what they want to say next. We are greeted as if we had interrupted a banquet to which we had not been invited. And this is not really surprising, given how few passengers there must be each week who get on at this station, and are headed in this direction. We go from one end of the coach to the other; and it is only after we have gone through the door at the back that we notice how that the moment of tension which had kept everyone behind us in suspense has now passed. Everything has gone back to normal.

　　We breathe a sigh of relief.

Then the train's violent start, which we had forgotten about in the engine car, takes us by surprise, and makes us turn from one wall to the other in search of something to hold on to. The toilet door bangs frantically against its frame. We are faced with a hurricane in a miniscule space. But there's no way of closing the door; there's not even the slightest remaining trace of a lock.

When the elements have calmed down we take a look inside the toilet. On the wall at the back is a notable piece of graffiti, a carefully inscribed message of recent date. It is written with the most beautiful lettering, which, from afar, seems like the calligraphy on a manuscript. Sadly the ink has run, making the message mainly illegible.

This is what is left:

15-III-80

Message to ETA: No Hitler, no Mussolini, no Franco. The Basques are just stupid oafs who'll never understand a thing... (here follows an extremely long and illegible paragraph)... fascism... like Suárez. Long Live the Republic.

But the most noticeable feature of the toilet —there is nothing left of the wash basin— is the bowl in which to release the body's waste. Eroded by every type of ferruginous water (well, that's one way of putting it), it is scored by fine striations of rust spilling out from what is left of the white enamel. The mouth of the bowl appears like a well head. Any passenger suffering from vertigo would be incapable of discharging here even the most discreet stream of urine. The sleepers on the track can be seen passing beneath you like the blades of a guillotine. There's no doubt about it, this is the Hullero's fifth window. Through this the Hullero has its exit to the sea, its escape route, its fire ladder. If this had truly been the Wild West, Hollywood might well have had Sitting Bull and his ferocious warriors coming up through here. Now that really would have been a surprise attack.

We make use of the stop at Quintana to move on to another third class coach. There are some free seats here, but none together. Fernando sits down besides an old man, while I walk further on until I find a seat next to a middle-aged woman.

The passengers seem just to have walked out of Sunday mass in a Castillian village. Quite a number of the men wear jackets, and even waistcoats; most of them cover their heads with berets. As for the women, most are elderly and dressed in black. There are also numerous young boys and girls. The whole coach appears to be made up of grandparents and grandchildren.

The benches are made of long slats with a respectable gap between them: thus after only a few kilometers the traveller ends up striped like a zebra.

163

I ask my neighbour:

"What's this village called?"

"Quintana. Afterwards comes Espinosa, and then Redondo, and then Sotoscueva."

"You know the line well then?"

"Of course! I do the journey every eight days!"

"Good lord! Every eight days! Then you must be quite at home here."

My neighbour, who is not dressed in black, and has a cream-coloured blouse with a little bow around her neck, has an attractive, rosy appearance. She could have been the sister of the woman travelling to Cistierna. Like her, she is short but compact, with well-distributed proportions; thinner perhaps than the other woman, she seems, however, more dynamic and possibly stronger. But her voice is just a teeny bit chirpy.

"Well, I do like the train. I'm from Reinosa, and I've a house down here. Now I come every eight days. In winter, every fifteen days."

The din of the Hullero makes conversation difficult. Children are shouting their heads off on all sides.

My neighbour explains to me why she has to go so often to Reinosa (to get there she has to alight at Las Rozas), but her words reach me in a fragmented state, just like the message to ETA in the toilet. For at times the Hullero breaks out into a series of metallic grating sounds of no apparent rational explanation (the train's speed seems the same as before, and we are not crossing any bridge, or going through any tunnel), but which sounds like someone desperately clearing his throat. Then, after the attack has passed, there is a moment of calm and relief during which the noise of the train is reduced to a civilized level. In one of those brief respites my neighbour assures me that we are running late due to the yellow engine, and that the blue one, which comes on other occasions, is much faster and better. As I have some inside knowledge of the matter, I would like to put her right on this; but the Hullero, which is having one of its ferocious throat-clearing fits, prevents me from doing so.

The noise does not decrease until we reach Espinosa, whereupon it suddenly ceases almost completely. The ensuing silence shamelessly exposes the sound of a mother shouting:

"You're going to fall off, you idiot!"

The child, riding on the back of her seat, in a white, lacy dress, bleats in protest. The mother replies to this with a short, sharp bark:

"Shut up!"

"This is an attractive village, isn't it?", I ask my neighbour.

My neighbour agrees:

"It certainly is. The whole of Bilbao and Vitoria comes to spend the summer here."

"Really?"

And my neighbour adds in her bird-like voice:

"Espinosa de los Ric...
FRA...

"This is a place for the rich."

There is a mass exodus of passengers, which makes my energetic neighbour put her head out of the window, and look restlessly backwards and forwards. I ask her:

"Many people get off here, don't they?"

But she's thinking out loud.

"It's just that we're stopping here for a bit… for a bit…"

Then she comes to a resolute decision:

"Well I'm not going to stay here without having my glass of beer."

And she speeds out of the coach, driven by a desire not just to calm her thirst, but somehow to prove that when it comes to drinking beer in Espinosa, not even the rich can intervene.

«The noise does not decrease until we reach Espinosa, whereupon it suddenly ceases almost completely»

The village, needless to say, has yet to be called Espinosa de los Ricos, but is still known as Espinosa de los Monteros, a name which alludes, some say, to the institution of the Monteros de la Cámara, or palace officials whose duty was to protect royalty at night-time. The story behind this dates back to the time of the Count of Castile Sancho García, who, to thank some minor member of the local nobility for saving his son, granted the guardianship of his house, person and family to the nobles of the vicinity. But it's also said that the

167

village is the ancient Cantabrian community of Mónega, which, when rebuilt by Alfonso VI, was given its present name on account of its many hawthorns (*'espinos'*).

In any case, it is traditionally thought that Castile had its origins here; and that, what is more, the territories that extend around and to the south of Espinosa are the true heartland of Old Castile. In the last years of the 8th century people from the other side of the mountains of Ordunte and Reinosa came to this area: some were Basques, and others Cantabrians, among whom were a magnate known as Lebato, and his wife Muniadona. A son of theirs established various towns and settlements around Espinosa de los Monteros, and in the Mena Valley. The manuscript mentioning his achievements is dated September 15, 800, and contains the first mention of the name of Castile.

«Its most important building is the Castle of the Velascos»

Dionisio Ridruejo, as an old Castilian, loved Espinosa. He says that it is an impressive place, what with its fortified houses, crenellated towers, and two important churches; and that its most important building is the Castle of the Velascos, Dukes of Frías —a fortress surrounded by the large poplars that dominate the whole district, and featuring a keep, (severe, rectangular, and with few openings) with a square guard tower reached by an external staircase.

168

"Castillo de los Duques"
José S. Carralero

Certainly the railway station of Espinosa is one of the most important along the whole line, with more than one platform, dwarf plane trees and a station buffet with a wide window looking out on to the main platform. The passengers from our train are all gathered in the buffet, frantically lifting up their arms to try and attract attention.

Fernando and I, now almost alone in the coach, feeling like castaways observing how their companions are tending to their own needs, are suddenly overcome with an insatiable thirst. We speedily alight from the train, and, even though we are the last at the bar, manage to grab a bottle of coke cola each.

The stationmaster blows his whistle, the Hullero answers in kind, and the platform is immediately emptied of passengers, just as if they had been pieces of paper blown away by the wind. When we think we have returned to our earlier seats, we discover we have entered another coach. Fortunately, very near the door, to the right of the aisle, there are two empty places, one in front of the other.

LUIS AND SO-AND-SO, TWO TRAVELLERS FROM BILBAO

W E SIT DOWN. The coach looks scruffy. A panel from the ceiling is half fallen off and is swaying with the movements of the Hullero. Fernando sits next to some old boy with a large beret, who has the nose and ears of the archetypical Basque. I do so next to a man barely in his forties who, his glance directed towards his lap, is absorbed in the task of smearing with grease a leather wine gourd.

«Our neighbours have to pull themselves in so that we can sit down»

Our neighbours, who have to pull themselves in up so that we can sit down, appear to have shrunk their tongues as well.

Referring obviously to the panel that hangs from the ceiling like a fan, I say:

"If it rains here we're going to get wet, aren't we?"

But there is no reply.

After a while Fernando says:

"The train's completely full, isn't it?"

But that doesn't work either, our two Carthusians

José S. Carvalho

172

show no reaction. And silence such as
theirs is truly surprising in a coach such
as this, where, if the Hullero allows it,
loquacity is the rule.

So, we continue drinking our
coke colas until I take the bull by the
horns and ask a direct question to my
neighbour, who's still immersed in his most
delicate of tasks.

"So that's lard you're using?"

173

And that finally does the trick. His reply is very quiet.

"No, I use bacon fat", he says, showing me a piece of fat between his fingers, "it's much softer."

My neighbour, of normal height, and not too burly, is dressed in a brown jersey and with beige trousers. His voice is youthful and crystal clear.

My eyes are fixed on his gourd, which he holds in his hands as if he were stroking a dog.

"You've got a good travelling companion there", I tell him.

And now that we've laid the first stone, the rest of the building goes up without difficulty.

"Do you often do this journey?"

"Well yes, I do it almost every month."

"Every month! And where are you going to, to Palencia?"

"No. To Santander. I get off at Montes Claros."

"Are you going home?"

"No, I'm only going to where the in-laws are. I usually go around the first of every month."

"To see your in-laws?"

"Yes, that's right; I normally go on days when the sky's clear."

"What province are we in now?"

But now it's the old boy who offers a reply. He has a deep voice, which seems to emanate from deep down.

"Burgos. This is Burgos."

And between the two of them they start listing the stations of Burgos and then of Santander. Sometimes they have to go back because they have left out one; and then they begin again as if they were reciting a chronology of Spain's Visigothic kings.

Behind the old boy, a group of four women of very different ages, keep up a continuous conversational hum, without pausing, without any change of tone, just the same motley superimposition of voices. One of them, with her back to the old boy, almost certainly the man's wife, not only can hear all that we are saying without neglecting her own gabbling group, but also —incredible though this might seem— is able to take part in the listing of stations.

"No, Luis", she says to the old boy, "after Pedrosa comes Citad."

The old man contains this interruption, and seems even amused by it. The man with the gourd laughs openly, and shows in process a gold tooth. The old boy is a stern figure, tall and slim; apart from the beret, he wears a red jersey, and a grey pair of trousers.

Outside, the greenery becomes lusher. Beech wood covers the mountains on both sides of the track.

"What mountains are these?", I ask my neighbour, who does not stop for a moment to rub the gourd.

"Around here… I don't really know the area. The leaves have all opened. It's very green. The last time I was here they hadn't opened yet."

"Where are you from?"

"From Bilbao. And my children were born in Bilbao as well. I've a lad who's seventeen. They were all born in Bilbao."

The old boy laughs.

"Why are you laughing", I ask.

"I too am from Bilbao. Or rather from Baracaldo."

The man with the gourd is quite aware of the special qualities of both the place he is about to visit, and the whole area through which the Hullero has to pass in order to get there.

"There's no way of taking my mother-in-law away from here".

"I'm not surprised", corroborates the old boy.

"In winter, with a good supply of wood, and a good fire, you can live like a god."

"Wood?", says the old boy, "There's as much here as you could ever want."

The Hullero is moving around. It's swinging its hips from side to side, like a crawling snake:

"Your beer is going to fall", says the man with the gourd to Fernando, referring to the bottle of coke cola the latter is holding in his hand. Then he asks:

"You've never been here before, have you?"

We explain to him what we are doing. He says:

"My father-in-law is seventy-six, and he's never left here."

"Almost from the same neck of the woods as my family", says the old boy. The other one continues:

"I know every place around here. In my spare time, I come here to have a look around. This train comes in handy for me. If you get on in Bilbao there's always a seat. It would be really bad lack if you had to stand. This time of year, it's usually empty, though in summer… In July, for instance, it's heaving, with people standing up and all."

As he speaks he continues greasing the gourd with all the concentration and tenacity of a watch-maker.

The Hullero stops:

"What's this place called?"

"Quintanilla del Rebollar", says the old boy.

Through the window we see the whitewashed, rectangular stones of what seems like a beautiful church, which is so close to the track that it could be a railway station.

«We see the whitewashed, rectangular stones of what seems like a beautiful church»

The stop makes the man with the gourd finally look up from what he is doing. And, as with those suffering from cataracts who can only focus on some microscopic detail, his vision settles again on Fernando's bottle of coke cola.

"Is it empty yet?", he says, indicating with his hands how he could take it away from him, and throw it out of the coach.

His gesture is a normal traveller's courtesy, just like helping someone take down their luggage. Fernando tells him:

"Let's wait until we get off."

Apeadero de Redondo
FRAGUAS

"There's no-one on the track", says the old man. "You won't hit anyone."

The Hullero begins to move off, and we hand over our empty bottles to our obsequious neighbours, who throw them out of the window. Then they get back to their seats, clearly relieved. The tall green branches of the poplars and oaks, so near to the track, bear pained witness to what the men have done.

I consult my list of stations, and don't find any mention of the last one.

"What did you say this station was called?", I ask.

"Quintanilla del Rebollar", answers the old boy. And since he sees me scrutinizing again the list, he explains:

«The tall green branches of the poplars and oaks, so near to the track, bear pained witness to what the men have done»

"The actual stop is called Redondo, but the village is Quintanilla del Rebollar."

The man with the gourd has become involved again in his delicate task. You cannot but admire his dedication. I ask him:

"What, do you always leave this job for the train?" No. You must be joking! It's just that I've been meaning to do it for ages. I just didn't have the time at home. At last, it's taking on a good colour. It was almost yellow before."

"What wine do you put in it?"

"From Valmaseda. And also from here. I had it half filled in Valmaseda, and then I refilled it here, because I had eaten a sandwich. And then when I

Quintanilla del Rebollar
José S. Carralero.

get to my parents-in-law, and that should be around two thirty, they'll ask me to go up and eat with them. But I always stay downstairs. My in-laws will shout: So-and-so come up and eat… So-and-so, come up here… and all that."

The man with the gourd has a peculiar way of speaking. He refers to himself as "So-and-so", and calls the place he's going to 'where the in-laws are."

"The Ebro runs through where the in-laws are. Its source is here, in Fontibre."

The old boy's wife, without tearing herself away from all the buzzing conversation of her group, shouts out:

"Luis, start preparing your things!"

«The Hullero stops in Sotoscueva»

The man with the gourd looks up, stares at the old boy, and shows his golden tooth.

Our neighbours have a friendship that was born on the train. They got to know each other on the journey, and, despite the difference in ages, or perhaps because of it, there's a great deal of sympathy between them. And indeed the old boy turns out to be the same age as the man with the gourd's father-in-law, which is no trivial coincidence as far as our friend is concerned.

The old boy tells us that he's getting off at Pedrosa, and then he talks about the tunnel at La Engaña, about the railways which links the Cantabrian with the Mediterranean. But the Hullero is overcome by another

Sotoscueva. Fraguas.

of its fits, and we only catch the tail end of his speech. His tone is complaining, sarcastic even.

"But that's just how things are in Bilbao… the things of Bilbao! Because instead of coming to Bilbao the tunnel goes to Santander. They should have done something about this by now."

The Hullero stops. The man with the gourd asks:

"Are you getting off here?"

"No. This is Sotoscueva."

The wife of the old boy, slight and flirty, goes back into the attack:

"Come on Luis, get my case down, now that we've stopped."

The man with the gourd shakes his head, creases his brow, and puts on an amused smile as he looks at the old boy.

On the board separating the seats from the lobby hang some framed advertisements. They are old, and out of date. 'Okal, the true pain-killer', 'Inter, the official television set'. In their day they were more modern than the Hullero, they were fashionable, but the Hullero has seen them off, has survived them.

We leave the case in the lobby, and sit down again. The train stays put.

"The journey is attractive, but long, isn't it?", I say.

The man with the gourd is not so sure:

"Of course, it's a bit...", and he pauses, before resuming in a rather confused fashion. "Now for me, to begin with, it used to be really difficult. But now, given of course the right..." Then he pauses again. "And yes...for instance today, don't you think? ...And if you did it again, say, in four or five days, it would be infinitely easier. And it's only three hours, you have to tell yourself."

Fernando and I agree.

The old boy says, sarcastically:

"Anyone who's healthy when he starts the journey ends up sick, and anyone who's sick ends up healthy. You get ill just from the jolts of the driver."

The man with the gourd adds:

"It used to be terrible. I've been doing this for twenty years. It used to be all smoke. With the steam trains you emerged from here completely black. It was terrible." And, as he says this, he shows his golden tooth, evidently amused.

"I've been doing this now for fourteen years", says the old boy, "and I can tell you that if you do this in winter your days are numbered. I went to Zorroza last week, because my granddaughter was having her first communion. There were three of us who went there. Now, if we were travelling today in the state we were then, we would barely be alive. Half the passengers never make it back to Bilbao. They're asphyxiated."

"By what?", we ask, taken back and alarmed.

"By the heat!", he says, as if this were the most normal thing possible. "We were travelling with all the windows open, and we still couldn't put up with the heat. What a terrible heat it was then!"

It occurs to the author that the Hullero is to trains what a young bull is to bullfights. To the passengers it is a source of conflicting emotions. You observe it with a certain paternalism; you put up with it, and love it as you do a child, but a young child, still hesitant in his speech and walk. It is an object of both hilarity and affection. A relic of the past and a caricature of a train, but it's a true and fully developed train, capable of daily fulfilling what it's intended for.

The passengers have the same attitude towards it as the spectators have towards one of those comic bullfights featuring dwarves and a matador who's a fireman. The tension does not result in drama, but in comedy. And yet a goring is always a goring, the sand is always sand, and blood is always blood.

"Did you say that you've been doing this for fourteen years?"

"No, well, I've been retired now for fourteen years."

From behind us you can here the admonitory voice of his wife:

"Thirteen! Thirteen years, Luis, thirteen!"

"Well, what's the difference? When working it's all the same. Now I don't remember anything."

The man with the gourd leans forward, smiling, with his golden tooth:

"He does not want to think so many years have passed."

"Take away a year or two, but don't do so anymore; don't take away any of the few years left to me. After the age of seventy-seven, no one can take away any of my years. If only I was forty. Seventy seven years have passed me by...", and the old boy lets out a laugh.

"Where did you use to work?"

"In the steelworks. In Altos Hornos. From 1902 up to now."

"You've been working from 1902 up till now?"

"No, no! I was born then!"

A Fleeting Vision of the Hearth

O SLÉ THE GUARD and Santiago Álvarez, the railway worker from Mataporquera, unexpectedly enter our coach. They have been calling us from the platform.

"Hey! Hey!", they continue shouting as they climb up on to the train in almost a single bound, and noisily open the door into the coach. The bewilderment of the passengers is transformed into a sudden silence.

The two men, out of breath, puffing away, manage to blurt out:

"The yellow locomotive is coming!"

But the passengers remain unsettled, struck dumb, and filled with expectation, without any magical cry of "Open, sesame!" having been uttered.

"The yellow locomotive! The yellow locomotive!"

Responding perhaps more out of courtesy than excitement, we rush to the back of the coach as if escaping from a fire. We have to see the yellow engine. But a ferocious noise breaks out. It's another train, another Hullero, one with a yellow engine, that is passing rapidly by us on the left. It passes in a stroboscopic flash. There's not even time to take a photo.

We remain at the back. And from Sotoscueva to Pedrosa we travel with Oslé and Sergio Álvarez. I ask Sergio about what he does on the train.

"I work as a...", he starts to answer.

But Oslé has already assumed the man's voice:

"A porter, he's a porter."

The Hullero winds its way in between mountains higher than a thousand metres. The landscape abounds in pastures, oaks and poplars.

It is a shame there's no time for a brief tour of this district of Sotoscueva. In almost every village there's a Romanesque church. But the most notable feature of the area is its rich troglodytic culture, which boasts of more than one Covadonga —the miraculous cave where the Reconquest is said to have started. Chuchi was saying that in Cornejo there is a river that disappears into a cave, and that this river might be the Cadagua, which breeches in this way the great wall of La Losa so as to come out in the Mena Valley and reach the Cantabrian coast. Perhaps Chuchi was referring to the caves of Cornejo, which are connected by way of a lake to those of Entrambos, where you will find the hermitages of San Bernabé and San Tirso (the patron saints of the area) as well as the council chamber of the local Town Hall.

In Pedrosa we help our friends, the old boy and his wife, down to the platform, and run to the goods van to change the camera film.

The goods van smells like a kitchen, a village kitchen, a rustic hearth.

Nazario is squatting over his cooking pot. His expression is smiling and resigned. He lifts up the lid and stirs the stew. We are reminded of Chuchi and his pot.

But this is different. The thick smell, the numerous utensils, the darker walls of the goods van, and the very peaceful attitude of Nazario, remind the author of a mother cooking. And our entering the goods van is done in a suitably respectful manner: we have penetrated right into the sacred hearth of the home, where the traditional village mother marks out her own territory.

«In almost every village of this district of Sotoscueva there's a Romanesque church»

And Nazario himself—though we have no doubt of his manly qualities— displays all the preoccupations of a mother. He remembers those who are not with us, he is interested in the people who work with the railway, he is concerned with the railway's fate, and he is the one who stores the family's memories:

"God knows if this railway is going to survive. For the moment it seems it will. But there was a time… Once there were a thousand six hundred of us working for it, and now I don't think we're more than four

189

Ajo Guareña.

José Camarero

hundred. There were once people everywhere, and now most places are empty.

The Hullero enters a tunnel, the longest tunnel of the line: it runs for a kilometre, ascending for the first half, descending for the second. In the goods van we feel as if our house had just suffered a power cut. The ceiling lamp gives off a poor light, like the reddish aura emanating from old, coal-fired cookers.

"The railway continued working in the civil war. Half of the line was in the hands of the Reds, and the other half was controlled by the Nationalists. It was divided like this because the front was here, at Dosante, where so many Italians died."

Nazario stirs the stew.

"It must be almost ready. If it's not hot enough, we won't be stopping here."

Bridge over the river Nela, next to Robredo Ahedo

The light returns. The rounded cumulus and the mackerel clouds have joined together to form a grey and uniform leaden mass, like a ceiling of humidity. The Hullero continues making its way through the mountains.

In Robredo Ahedo we get out of the goods van to go back to the passenger coaches.

"Come back in Arija for your lunch", Nazario reminds us from the window.

e el río Nela
obredo, Ahedo
FRAGUAS

DOMITILA, WHERE ARE YOU GOING?

W E ENTER ONCE AGAIN the first class coach. In the rows of double seats, to the left of the aisle, are seated a young woman and a three-year-old girl, one in front of the other. On the other side of the aisle is an old woman with black clothes, a woollen jacket, and her hair tied back in a bob. Fernando occupies the free seat in front of her; I sit next to the girl.

«We barely had the time to see some greyish burning bushes to the side of the train»

"What's your name", I ask her.

The mother proudly answers:

"Beatriz. I'm called Beatriz."

The young mother is going to Mataporquera, to spend a few days with her parents.

"To be in my own home", she says.

She and her daughter are travelling very well dressed and groomed.

To our left there's a sudden blast of heat, intense and fleeting, which fills the coach with an acrid smell

195

of burning. This brief fire —we barely had the time to see some burning bushes to the side of the train— seems to have denuded the landscape; now it is treeless and pale, like some stretch of moor land.

"Hasn't this changed?", I say.

"It seems always the same to me", says the mother, "Or perhaps worse." But she is referring to the Hullero.

"Well, it's not that bad in here", I reply.

"But if we were on the benches…", she says. "When I go back on Sunday, there'll be no seats here, and I'll have to sit on the benches. It will be full all the way from León."

I tell her that we are in fact going to León.

"You're going all the way to León, she asks in a tone that is both surprised and pitying."

The older woman says:

"I'm going to Guardo", and she looks out of the window, uninterested in the conversation that might arise from this, anxious as she is only to maintain her isolation. There's a touch of sadness, almost of fear, in her attitude.

The mother of Beatriz, instead, is very chatty, and keen to find any way to break the tedium of the journey. She has a rounded and cheerful face. But there's something wily and slightly untrusting about her eyes.

"What are you doing, taking photos so that they can improve the train, or what?"

I give a brief summary of what we're up to, and all seems suddenly clear to her:

"You're Basques! Aren't you?"

I tell her we're from León, and her rounded face assumes an ironic smile. Her eyes are almost burning from scrutinizing us.

"So, you're not from Bilbao?"

To swear we're not would be too much, so I merely repeat what I've said.

"No. No, we're not from Bilbao. We're from León."

It's one o'clock in the afternoon. Apart from us, few others are talking in the coach. A general lassitude, dejection almost, has set in.

We reach Soncillo. No-one gets off, and few people show any interest in the station. But this unusual calm cannot last. Within moments a small and vivacious woman —a true ball of energy— has burst into the coach, and is standing next to us. She has a powerful head, grey and curly hair, a broad and open face, a commanding nose, a strong jaw and a body that is short but solid. This ball of energy wears a smock with ample pockets, a blouse and a black-spotted jacket.

"Good-day, ladies and gentlemen. I've got some of the most delicious things for you today."

Her timing could not be better. Gastric juices are flowing through the stomach like hares running to safety.

199

The young mother tells me quietly:

"It's Domitila, the sweets woman. Later she goes back on the mail coach from León".

"Come on, all of you, I've got lovely little things today for all you boys and girls. Who wants to take a card?"

"I'll take two", I say.

She gives them to me.

"How much do I owe you?"

"Fifty pesetas."

"You're joking. For that amount of money the prize better be worth it."

"Let's wait and see."

Domitila moves around like a mouse. Swift and over-powering, she has a word for everyone, without neglecting, every so often, to address the whole coach in an oratorical tone.

«Domitila presents him the pack with a hand that is as large and plump»

"Come!", she says imperiously to Fernando, "you can cut the pack."

"Have you sold every card?"

"Every single one."

Domitila presents Fernando the pack with a hand that is as large and plump as a Spanish omelette. Fernando's seat is the one nearest the door, thus obliging Domitila to turn her back to almost everyone in the coach. But not even we, the people closest to her, can clearly see what she's doing.

200

Domitila says:

"Come on there, you've won."

"Who's won?", I ask.

"This gentleman. The one with the spades."

The mother of Beatriz laughs in an irritated way.

"Well, well!", she says.

"But announce it, madam", I tell Domitila, "so that everyone knows."

"I'm not going to announce or enunciate it, he's s won and that's it. The man with the spades has won!"

The prize consists of a diminutive green plastic basket containing two packets of sweets. Fernando opens a packet and offers it round. First to his neighbour, the old woman with her hair in a bun; then to Beatriz, and then to her mother. We all take a sweet.

And then Domitila is off again:

"Come on, come on, it's another round! Who wants clubs? Come on, anyone for diamonds? You, sir, you have to choose again. This goes quickly, this does."

I buy another card, and I ask her where she's going. To answer me, she softens her voice, and drops the tone she uses for her work.

"I'm going to Arija, and then I go back on the mail coach".

This time the woman with the bun does the cutting. Her hands are large, white and wrinkled.

On the ring finger of her right hand she wears two wedding rings.

Domitila knows better than anyone who's going to get the prize.

"This lady has won!"

It's Beatriz's mother. Her face shines like an apple.

"Well, thank goodness for that!"

Beatriz's mother receives another tiny basket. She too opens one of the bags, and offers us a sweet.

Domitila does not let up:

"Come on, come on, we're playing again!"

While showing her in my fingers a twenty-five peseta coin (to buy another card), I start asking her questions. She says:

"I now live in Pedrosa, and I have a place in Bilbao."

Her voice has become for a moment very deep, dry and rapid. But then immediately it's back to being a trumpet.

"Let's start again. I've some packets of almonds. Do you want another card, lady? Now we'll get someone else to cut them for you", she tells the old woman.

I take out another coin, and ask her:

"So Domitila, you do all your business here?"

"Me? Yes, here in the train. One hour in the train, and that's it. In winter, nothing at all."

Beatriz's mother is almost closing her eyes to

look at me. She might as well point to me with her finger. She seems to have discovered something:

"You are from Bilbao, aren't you? You're Basques."

Damn it! The author is disconcerted. On what does she base her evidence? Sabino Arana wrote that the "Biscayan physiognomy is noble and intelligent; while the Spanish one is inexpressive and severe. The Biscayan is handsome and manly in his gait; the Spaniard either not know how to hold himself properly (conscripts, for instance), or, if he does so, he's effeminate, like a bull-fighter." Has our physiognomy given us away? Has Fernando's height of one hundred and eighty-five centimeters? Or my weight of over one hundred kilos? The author cannot deny that he feels flattered.

To our right appears the Ebro reservoir, as grey as the sky that drops down to it. We can make out in the background a dark, cloud-covered mountain, some small sailing boats, tiny and fast. Or is that what they are? The whole landscape is leaden, heavy, wintery.

"Diamonds!", shouts Domitila. And the prize goes this time to our neighbour, the old woman.

Domitila rushes towards her. The old woman receives her prize with two hands, as if worried that it's going to fall on the floor. Her expression barely changes; the wrinkles on her face hardly tighten; and her eyes remain blankly fixed and not even moistening behind her glasses. Only her body —and this is barely noticeable—bends and tenses to receive the prize (a packet of almonds) in her lap. And there it will stay, for what is left of the journey, hidden, caught, protected by her two white, worn hands of ice.

Domitila, who has been employing her commercial skills among those in the front seat, is back once again. She is addressing me:

"The diamonds, you've still got your card with the diamonds."

I search through my pockets. Nerves are paralyzing me. Domitila is intimidating me with her formidable presence; she is disturbing me with her instant changes of manner. Finally I find the card with the diamonds.

She snatches it out of my hand, and holds it immediately above her head.

«To our right appears the Ebro reservoir, as grey as the sky that drops down to it»

"There's one more card here. Who wants it?"

"I do", I say.

"Come on. Someone cut the cards over here."

The mother of Beatriz bends over to say to me:

"I'm not surprised she's got a flat in Pedrosa. She must be reeling in it. What with everyone here spending their lives getting ready to hand her over twenty-five pesetas."

The mother of Beatriz sees the price of the cards in terms of some traveller's tax, just like the ones you had to pay in medieval fiefdoms.

The reservoir can now be seen as broad and rough,

Et pantans.

Lois Canales

just like the sea; the sailing boats can be made out more clearly.

Domitila returns, insatiable:

"Let's see, I've got two more cards left."

"You're back again", I say.

"You're all a bit boring today", she says in the hard voice of someone who is ready to put up daily with infinitely more unpleasant realities.

"You don't want another one, madam?", she asks the old woman with the bun, "There aren't two left, there are three!"

But Domitila has to go back and harangue the front of the coach.

"Come on, come on! You're all so boring today."

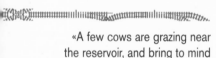

«A few cows are grazing near the reservoir, and bring to mind some Nordic scene»

Fernando complains that there's not enough light to take photos, and Beatriz's mother opens her mouth in a very knowing way.

"Come on, tell the truth, you're from Bilbao."

We have to laugh. What can we say? Sabino Arana also wrote that the 'Biscayan is hard-working… the Spaniard lazy and unreliable… The Biscayan is no good as a servant, he is born to be a master… The Spaniard needs from time to time a foreign invasion to civilize him…' What on earth must this good lady be seeing in us?

It goes without saying that we are incapable of pretending to be what we are not. The mother be-

us del Ebro.
FRAGUAS

comes once again serious and scrutinizing. She finally seems to have admitted defeat. We note an immediate decline in the way she treats us.

"Aren't you going to photograph the cows?"

A few cows are grazing near the reservoir, and bring to mind some Nordic scene, some scene from a land of fogs and fjords, and of dark and mysterious lakes.

And now that she has found herself among equals, she can say what she likes:

"This was where two engineers from Bilbao drowned. They had come to hunt ducks."

The reservoir is dark and choppy, with some white crests, just as if it were a turbulent sea.

The mother of Beatriz repeats herself:

"Two engineers from Bilbao, well I don't know what could have happened. Their boat must have capsized, or something like that."

The tragedy is doubly awful for the fact that the men were not only engineers, but from Bilbao as well, a distinction that is like awarding them an A+.

Such loss of life appears so irreplaceable that even the old woman with the bun, ostensibly absorbed in the contemplation of the landscape, feels obliged to comment:

"It appears that they did not know how to swim."

But Beatriz's mother does not go for this theory.

"No, they certainly knew how to swim. What must have happened is that some whirlpool dragged them under. The reservoir is really treacherous."

We all stare at this murderous, grey expanse of water — this restless, ominous expanse whose waters extend almost up the edge of the railway bank, and seem to knit their brow as the Hullero passes.

Beatriz's mother adds:

"They say that a drowning person is so frightened of dying that he takes with him anyone he's with. In Mataporquera this happened to two girls. They went to have a swim after just finishing eating. Their digestion was stopped. And then they were found bound together in an embrace."

LUNCH WITH THE FAMILY

W E REACH ARIJA. Domitila rushes towards us from the front seats, with her mouse-like stance. She is getting off. We help her with her unwieldy load: two wooden cases older than the Hullero, as heavy as lead, and with edges that cut.

We alight as well.

How can we possibly forget what Nazario told us from the window of the goods van?

«This is where the Hullero fills its saddle bags every day with nearly a thousand tons of sand »

Arija still falls within the province of Burgos. This is where the Hullero fills its saddle bags every day with nearly a thousand tons of sand from the reservoir destined for the Spanish Glass Works of Llodio, in Vizcaya. Thus, nowadays, Arija is one of the most active places along the line.

The station building is itself quite notable. Solid and spacious, it has two floors built of rectangular blocks of grey stone painted white in the joins. It

Acija
Juil-Canulus.

has a pitched roof, and —a real sign of the station's importance— a metalwork canopy.

The sky and the reservoir have the same dark and ash-like appearance, without any break between them. The sun seems lost in the cottony background of either the one or the other. It is cold.

We run towards the goods van. Nazario and Oslé are waiting for us.

"Come on you two, come on."

The goods van turns out to be wonderfully welcoming. Nazario cheerily opens for us the doors of his house. He seems to have been waiting for us before laying the table. And with exceptional care, he now improvises such a table out of a small bench. Using a newspaper as a table cloth, he spreads this across the wooden slats, and puts on top of this an exceptionally large earthenware dish. Then he hands out a spoon to each of us, and tells us where we have to sit.

"You there. And you there. We can't just sit down any old how. And you, Luis, over there."

Fernando sits on top of the safe, which has no lock. I do so over another, smaller one, also of black metal. Everything in the goods van is black. Oslé has to work, and so needs a special seat allowing him to keep watch on the passengers entering and leaving the train; thus he sits down at the end of the bench, next to a little window. He does not take his hat off.

We are interested in how he's heating the pot.

"We use charcoal", says Nazario emphatically. "This burner is five years old. I had another one, but it broke; and they had to make me a new one in the workshops at Valmaseda."

When everyone's at the table, Nazario finally pours out the contents of the pot into the large dish.

"Come on, come on, let's eat", he says.

The stew astonishes us: kidney beans, potatoes, bay leaves, meat. All the colours that are lacking in the goods van are shining inside it. The dish could not have been better had our mothers made it.

"Come on, come, this is going to get cold."

Nazario is unable to sit down and relax: whether standing, squatting, or perched precariously on a small black box, like that of shoeshine boy, he is concerned only to make sure that everything is right, and that no-one goes hungry.

The smell of the stew transports us far away, and for a moment the author thinks that he and Fernando are the sons of a good, honest couple who sit down each day to eat with their family.

Nazario cuts the bread from a large loaf, and hands us each a piece.

"If you put it underneath the spoon", he says, "the broth won't drip on to the floor."

The construction of the Ebro reservoir (which was opened in 1945) involved the diversion of the line so that this would not suffer the same fate as the various villages and hamlets in Burgos and Santander that lie today beneath the waters. The new route —with viaducts that cut off some of the corners of the reservoir— skirts the water's banks for eighteen kilometers, thus briefly turning the Hullero into a coastal train. That this stretch of the line should bring to mind the shores of Lake Baikal —which the Transiberian follows for a whole day— should not be thought of as impudence on the part of the Hullero. This grey spring day, oppressive and foggy, cold and damp, seems a portent of harsh and icy winters. And when the winters get that bad you could easily use the Hullero for the exteriors of films such as *Doctor Zhivago*.

While we are eating, we cannot see outside. We ask, none the less, to be warned when we near a sunken church whose tower is said to rise above the waters. Nazario will look out for it as well.

We all dip our spoons into the dish, making sure always to keep to the same side.

The Hullero stops in Llano. Oslé keeps an eye on what's happening from the window. He comments:

"The source of the Ebro is near here. At Reinosa, some seventeen kilometers from here."

The author gives up trying to have a look at the countryside. Once he is seated at table, and so near to the ground, he has no desire to get up. But he regrets not doing so. The enormous expanse of water has a morbid appeal for him. The lack of brightness, the disturbing, uniform greyness which appears to emanate from the reservoir, has a strange hold over him. Time will surely give these waters the legends they still lack; and it is possible that one day the fishes here will have human heads: the accusatory heads of those dead people whose eternal rest has been disturbed by the flooding of the cemeteries.

Lunch passes quietly. There's harmony in this family. The father is serious, and circumspect; the mother obliging and understanding; the children restless and curious.

We speak about Domitila, who they all know. We speak about the climate of this area, which is cold all the year round. We speak about the reservoir, which will soon supply water to Santander as well.

«The new route has viaducts that cut off some of the corners of the reservoir»

Nazario passes round the gourd to everyone in turn. And no stew has ever gone down as well as this one, or been so warming.

To the right of the Hullero are the waters of the reservoir; and to the left the wooded slopes of the mountains. The leafy branches of the oaks flash past the windows like the forms in a Chinese shadow play, and take away much of what light there is on this side of the train.

Nazario is worried we're not eating.

"So you don't like this, eh? Eat, eat, otherwise it'll all be thrown away."

Puente entre Anjas y Las Rotas
FRAGUAS

"...Torre sumergida..."
Jou S. Cavalero

And the conversation continues.

"There are some people around here who earn eighty thousand pesetas just from fishing crabs", says Nazario, making some vague gesture with his arm.

"Really?"

"And I can quite believe it", declares Nazario, shaking his head and arching his brow. Oslé, the guard, remains silent.

Suddenly Nazario gets up.

"The church tower's just coming up!"

He must have smelt the building, for he certainly can't see it. But it takes its time in coming. And, when it does, the Hullero whistles. It's made of stone. It's sturdy and beautiful, with a slate spire, and an ironwork weathervane. It's graceful and elegant, but does not seem especially old (what a shame!). It rises out of the water like the hand of a drowned man, like the standing stone on a tomb.

We sit down again. The Hullero reduces its speed. Oslé says:

«The church tower rises out of the water like the hand of a drowned man»

"Las Rozas. About three kilometers from here the reservoir comes to an end."

The station is on the other side of the track, and Oslé wants to cross over to the other window. But Nazario stops him from doing so.

"I'll keep watch, Luis, I'll keep watch. Just stay where you are."

Nazario looks out of the window, and reports:

"Someone's entered the green coach, Luis."

And then:

"Someone's just got off, Luis."

"From the last coach?"

"No, from the last but one, I think."

The Hullero moves off again, and we continue eating. Nazario thinks we haven't eaten enough.

"You don't like this, do you?"

"It's absolutely delicious."

"Then eat then, eat. No-one's eating. We're going to have to throw it all away."

"Do you always make the same dish?"

"It's important always to eat hot food here. Some days we have beans and meat. Yesterday, we ate salt cod and chickpeas. Sometimes it's rabbit. You throw in what you've got."

The earthenware dish is very deep, and we keep on dipping our spoons into it, filling up our bellies with its fulsome flavours, eating far more than we want so not as to offend Nazario.

The author spares a thought for Chuchi, whom he pictures on his own, eating as he drives the engine. He's another member of this family who now lives alone, earns his bread by himself.

Nazario says admiringly:

"Chuchi? Chuchi eats the same as the four of us put together. And he drinks the same! These Basques were born only to eat and drink!"

"But their food doesn't fill you", says Oslé, carefully choosing his words. "When I'm there I have my lunch, and then I have to eat again almost immediately."

"We're now getting to the dam", says Nazario. "This dam's a beauty."

He gets up and points it out to Fernando.

"Look, if you want take a photo, why don't you do so of that part over there, where the water's rushing out?"

Then he announces to us:

"Now we're going to cross the real Ebro."

The Hullero crosses the line's longest bridge, which was blown up by the Republicans during the war. The Ebro here is deep and narrow, as if, instead of water, it carries an acid which is eating its way across the landscape. Poplars line its steep banks.

The Hullero is back again among mountains. Oak woods cover the slopes on either side of the railway bank.

«The Hullero crosses the line's longest bridge. The Ebro here is deep and narrow»

"Okay, then", says Nazario, "I take it no-one wants any more. Now we can get on to the second course."

"What, there's something else?"

"Of course! We'll just have to throw this away!"

Nazario takes the earthenware dish, goes up to the window, and tips the stew outside.

"That's got rid of that. If no-one wants it, there's no other choice but to throw it away."

What can you say? The author had never imagined that the act of throwing away was going to be so literally intended. Nazario now rinses the

"Puente sobre el Ebro"
Luis Caballero

dish with water, dries it with a cloth, and puts it back
again on the improvised table. From the pot he
goes on to extract three enormous chorizos, an
abundance of meat, and the most enticing chunks
of bacon fat.

Oslé goes back to what he was saying before:

"The food up there is very insipid. I eat the
same quantities as here, and I'm hungry almost
immediately. There's a world of difference between
eating here and eating in Valmaseda."

Nazario would have liked to have cooked
something better:

"I have some cod and a potato I could have thrown
in."

The dish looks like something out of a publicity
campaign to promote traditional country cooking.
Nazario, standing besides us, offers us all a fork.

"The chorizo looks really good."

"Eat, eat, we've got absolutely plenty."

And that's no exaggeration! Fernando and I cut
up a chorizo and share it between the two of us.

"You're hardly eating, you two", says Nazario.
"We're going to have to throw it all away. Come
on, at least have something to drink."

I bring the gourd near to me, and let the wine
flow into my mouth.

"Squeeze it as much as you want", says Nazario.

The small black box next to his feet continues
to intrigue us.

"It's a telephone", says Nazario.

"Do you use it?"

"Of course!", he says, nimbly crossing over to the other side of the goods van to pick up a pole with a cable wrapped around it. "This cable can be attached to the telephone line."

"Have you ever used it?"

"Of course, many times. When the track was so bad it was almost falling off, and there was no way of driving on any further. We just stayed here sprawled out until help came."

It does not matter that we are now completely full. The chorizo is delicious.

"Eat, eat", he says, "otherwise we're going to have to throw the lot away."

«Near the stop at Montes Claros is a Dominican monastery»

We arrive at Montes Claros. Oslé looks outside. Undoubtedly he's going to spot our friend with the gourd, who was going to "where his in-laws are". Then, after the train has started off again, Oslé says:

"From here to the León basin it's all mines". He's speaking from the corner of the bench, with a piece of bread in one hand, and a chunk of bacon fat in the other. "Salinas, mines; Cervera, mines; Castrejón mines; Villaverde, mines; Santibáñez, mines; Guardo, mines; Matallana, mines…"

Near the stop at Montes Claros is a Dominican monastery. The Hullero is possibly the monks' only

means of communication during the winter months.

In the dish there's still one whole chorizo, most of the meat, and a good portion of bacon fat.

Oslé eats very slowly, with some difficulty, as if he had some serious gap in his teeth. Fernando has given up eating some time ago. Nazario can't bear seeing me hesitate.

"Eat, eat."

"I can't any more", I announce.

"Then we're going to have to throw it all away", he says with a tone of resignation.

And now there's no doubt whatsoever about what he intends to do. He approaches the table, picks up the dish, takes it to the window, and then —now you see it, now you don't— throws all the food on to the oaks.

It's time now for dessert. Fernando holds up Domitila's bag of sweets:

"Do you want one?"

"No! No!"

Sweets are not for parents. Oslé offers us some oranges. Nazario, some pears. We have already begun on the sweets, and turn down the fruit. Oslé says:

"Well I'm not going to throw away the orange."

Nazario takes a banana, and Oslé peels an orange. We speak about their jobs with the railway. Oslé has spent his whole life on the Hullero, "except for four months, when I was in Valencia, working on the railways there."

Nazario's story is similar:

"All of us here have been with this railway for twenty or thirty years."

We have now stood up to stretch our legs, and can see, through the left window, a tiny, distant village in between the mountains and the grazing fields.

"Aldea de Ebro."

Oslé offers us again an orange. Once again we refuse.

"Well, I'm certainly not going to throw away this orange, damn it", he says, offended, "It's worth seventy five pesetas at the railway discount store."

It's amazing what inertia can do to these railway workers! There was little enough excuse to throw away the beans, and even less to chuck out the chorizos. But there is no excuse at all for getting rid of the oranges. And, nonetheless, Oslé, clearly gripped by an impulse to throw them out of the window, holds this impulse back by reminding himself of their market price.

«This railway is extraordinary. It's always going through mountains and beautiful green scenery»

It then occurs to the author that —given that we are not flying in a plane at an altitude of 9,000 metres, when the smallest hole could create the most dramatic effects of suction— there must be in the Hullero some supernatural, centrifugal force compelled to push everything through the window.

Aldea de Ebro still hovers in the distance, looking

like a toy placed against a background of green mountains.

"Over there, that's where the Ebro goes. Through those mountains."

"This railway is extraordinary. It's always going through mountains and beautiful green scenery."

"This Railway was a bloody gold mine, its owners made millions", says Oslé

"Everybody got rich; then, it was all over", Nazario concludes.

Oslé is waiting for the arrival of the inspector:

"He didn't come yesterday because it was a holiday. Perhaps he'll come today. Everything's all in order, but you've still got to keep him informed."

Thus, on reaching Los Carabeos, he gets off, and goes back to the passenger coaches.

We start going again, and Nazario forces me to sit down on the bench.

"Sit down, I insist", he says, not allowing me to give my place up.

The earthenware dish has heated up the bench in a way that has made it unbearable. Nazario says:

"We're now getting to a really important town: Mataporquera. We normally stop there for half an hour. But today we'll be on our way again almost as soon as we get there. We're running late."

Then he puts on some glasses, and starts arranging some papers:

"These are all going to stay here", he says, alluding

to them. "Our other headquarters is here in Santander. This is the service chart. And here's the route chart. No, they've certainly got everything under control. But this is only half of the paperwork. I'll have to do the same again from Mataporquera to León. And all these reports: this one has to be signed by the driver, this one by the guard…"

He finishes writing and places the papers in his jacket pocket. He goes up to the window. The mountains are now impressively bare, with only the slightest hint of green, and some bushes of broom. Rocks and boulders protrude like pimples.

"We're now getting to the pass in between Mataporquera and Reinosa, the Pozazal pass. There's a tunnel for the Renfe trains. Over there, can't you see it? It's freezing here the whole year round."

Parallel to the railway bank, above the Hullero, rise some snow breaks. These consist of horizontally arranged planks of wood attached to vertical iron beams. Almost all the wood has been destroyed by fire. You would think that the war has not yet ended.

"Here, just as we enter Mataporquera, is the cement factory; on the other end   of the town is the factory that has…What do you call it?.. The stuff that makes iron hard… I've forgotten what they call it… Manganese!"

The voice of Nazario is sharp, and slightly tremulous. But no matter how he speaks, whenever he refers to his surroundings, he seems always to do so in a way that makes them appear somehow alien. His conscience forces him to distance himself from all that is not his, to make everything around him seem constantly far away. But this distance he maintains has also something of the bewilderment of a child lost in the contemplation of machines, constructions, factories...

Mataporquera comes into view, still a long way away.

"I lived here as a lad", he says, before adding.

"It's an important town. I had an accident..."

He shows me his right hand, which is missing his ring finger, and then arches his brow and opens his kind and dreamy eyes.

"Of course, I had to leave all this. And I went to Barcelona, to work in the Seat factory; it was a good job, working on the electrics. But I wasn't happy there. Then I was drawn back to León, I can't get away from the place. The railway had to take me on again, because of my finger. Because it would have been difficult to get in otherwise... I have a son who's trained as a secondary school teacher, and there's no way he can get a job. The head of the railway staff —he's one of us, he's from León!— has eaten here with me. The day I see him again, he's going to have to listen to me. You get wise with age. You can study all you want, take exams, have a career, but railways are complex things. You get wise from all the years of working on them."

MATAPORQUERA,
A STOP FOR REFRESHMENT

WE'RE NEARING THE STATION of Mataporquera, which is used also by Renfe, making it the most important stop on the whole line. Approximately half way along the route, it is where the trains going in either direction meet up.

"There's the other train", enthuses Nazario, excited either by the fact that it has arrived before us, or else by his being oblivious to the lack of any surprise element in his daily encounter with the familiar train. "Now, it's going to have to unload. If you want, you can go and have a coffee."

«This station is used also by Renfe, making it the most important stop on the whole line»

After the overpowering stew, the prospect of a coffee is a highly tempting one, and we consider it. We then jump out of the coach with our minds made up. But Nazario is becoming worried.

"You're going to have to be quick. No more than five minutes. You'll have to rush."

This is a strange contrast to Chuchi's attitude,

237

when he told us in Bercedo: "No rush, eh?". But we are good children, and turn down the idea of coffee. We don't want to worry Nazario. Besides the buffet is not even in the station. You've got to walk a few yards, leave the building by a side door, then cross a road.

On the platform there is much coming and going. Oslé, the guard, is heading towards the buffet in the company of one of the passengers.

"Go on, go on", Nazario now tells us, "you can go with him. And come back with him."

Fernando stays behind. He's decided to prowl around the station searching for subjects to photo-graph. Nearby, the enormous chimneys of the cement factory billow out great clouds of white smoke against the grey sky. The wider tracks of the Renfe, to the Hullero's left, are like the father's shoes in comparison with those of the son.

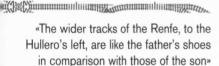

«The wider tracks of the Renfe, to the Hullero's left, are like the father's shoes in comparison with those of the son»

The buffet is also a grocer's, and its shelves are lined with tins. The television set, high up above a corner, to the left of the entrance, is like a torture to the ears.

Oslé's companion, about fifty years old, in a brown suit and tie, takes his coffee in the truly authentic way: he adds a glass of brandy. Oslé, not wishing to be left out, orders a cigar, which is immediately seconded by the other man. It looks as if it's going to be an

Matsporquer a
mediodía
FRAGUAS.

afternoon of truancy. I treat them: one hundred pesetas in all, for the three coffees, the glass of brandy, and the two cigars, tip included.

We speak about the journey, and what is left of it, without the two of them reaching any agreement about how many kilometers are left. Then they change subject and talk about a mutual friend.

"We went to school together. I haven't seen him in forty years", comments Oslé's companion, before saying to me, "One's earliest years are never forgotten."

On the wall behind the bar hang some pictures: they are colour photos of snowy landscapes. They could be of Russia, Canada, even Mataporquera. I ask a blonde lady helping her husband behind the counter about them. She appears to be the proprietress. But it's Oslé's companion who answers. His reply is completely unexpected, and spoken in a tactlessly high voice.

"This has to be the ugliest village on the face of the earth."

The proprietress, blonde and still young, continues washing glasses in front of us, with an unshaken expression.

"Let me say it again", says Oslé's companion in an even louder voice. "This is the ugliest and most horrible village on the face of the earth." Then, pausing to see if he has attracted everybody's attention, adds, "But it's marvelous in winter."

The woman raises her brow. The man continues talking:

"Not really. If was being completely honest, I would have to say that this village has just one thing you can say about it. It's extremely cold. The weather is rarely good here. If it's cold you freeze to death, if the sun's out, you burn yourself…"

The woman, who is now drying the glasses, smiles faintly, and joins in quite naturally:

"And then we fill this place up with shit."

The bewilderment now of the author knows no bounds:

"Why?", I ask her.

"Because there's a cement works, and another factory making chemical products and the like."

The Hullero whistles. Twice. Everyone begins hurrying in the bar. Oslé has taken out a large handful of coins which he wants to exchange for notes. He does not lose his calm.

I go back with his companion towards the train. He takes me by the arm, and confides into my ear an important piece of information:

"Do you want to know the average speed of this train?"

Though he has stopped walking, he is not waiting for my reply.

"28.59 kms an hour", he says.

I stare at him admiringly. To calculate the slowness of the Hullero with such precision is truly a labour of love. He adds:

"I made this calculation yesterday in my office."

"Do you also work on the railways?"

"No. I'm with General Spanish Electrics. I'm a programmer for domestic machines. I work in Bilbao, in Galibo. I'm on my way to visit a sister who lives in Barruelo de Santullán. I take the train because I haven't got a vehicle of my own."

Skinny and dark, with shiny black eyes, he's a man whose verbal outpourings display a precious turn of phrase. We're now walking in front of the engine, whose noise is deafening us.

"Now that shows the sort of pull we command", he says, stopping again. "The train is actually waiting for us."

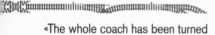

«The whole coach has been turned into the most colourful dining-car»

The coach has undergone inside a complete transformation. Though the usual, half-hour stop for lunch has been cancelled, because of the delay, the whole coach, as if obeying some inaudible bugle call, has been turned into the most colourful dining-car. The passengers seem like cheerful guests at a wedding banquet. Everyone is eating and drinking. The reclining seats have now been given over to a display of popular foods. Plates, knives and glasses are all glistening, and the colours of the kitchen and the market place are everywhere. What a feast! What abundance! It is as if each passenger was a magician who has conjured up on his seat tomatoes, peppers, apples, oranges, steaks, French and Spanish omelettes, chorizos and bread… This multiplicity of culinary delights has brought into the carriage the atmosphere of a picnic, a festive pilgrimage, a country outing.

And the lunch has still some way to go. And the after-lunch activities will almost certainly be excessively protracted and merge into an unusually long siesta.

This train belongs to the past; and its passengers are those Spaniards of the 1950s whose bags were largely taken up with food for the journey.

The man with me is greeted with merriment by the other passengers.

"And we thought we'd left without you", they say, their mouths full of food.

The man, standing now right in the centre of the coach, repeats emphatically and jovially what he has just said to me:

"It's just that we have a lot of pull, and the train was waiting for us."

Then he goes down the coach, wishing everyone an enjoyable lunch. He seems like a town councilor in the middle of an election campaign.

Oslé arrives, and transmits to me in his monotonous voice the following information:

"Until I get on, the train won't start. Whistle all it might, it has to wait until I arrive. It won't go until I do so. The inspector was there."

The Hullero finally starts up. I sit down, to the left of the aisle, next to the window. Oslé takes a seat next to me. The noisy tavern sounds of lunch continue. The train croaks, hisses, and hammers against the track, but soon attains a bearable level of noise that is almost capable of rocking one asleep. However, Oslé never stops talking even when digesting:

"Many skiers from Bilbao use this line, especially up to Espinosa. But there are still many people who do the journey by car. Even though there's increasingly less advantage in doing so. There's no better way of going from Bilbao to León than this one. If you went on the electric train you'd be forking out one thousand eight hundred, almost two thousand pesetas; this train costs you only six hundred and seventy. And if you use the Express, you have to do a really roundabout route, and change at Venta de Baños. It takes eight hours. This train takes at present ten and a half hours; but we could easily cut off an hour and half, even as the train is now. Might eventually do it in eight hours. We've still got five hours left. We're half way."

Never taking his cap off, and puffing on his cigar between interminable paragraphs, he maintains the same even, monotonous stance, like that of a coachman in the driver's seat.

"After Mataporquera we're immediately climbing again. The track you can see is still the same as before, it's just that we've done a big loop. Look at all the oaks."

Oslé points to everything as if it were his, and displays all the indifference of someone who has owned them for many years.

"This service would definitely improve if they brought back coal, if they reopen the mines."

Oslé travels next to me as if he were inspecting all the corners of his estate on horseback.

"The Villablino railway still runs on coal. We used to have two of the engines that Villablino now has, the Two hundred and fifty three, and the One hundred and fifty two. These trains don't have names, the steam ones all did. I know the names by heart. Number One was *León*; number Two *Palencia*; number Fifty-five, *Luis de Salazar;* number Fifty-six, *V. de Zavalinchaurreta,* an engineer who used to work here; number One hundred and thirty, *Antonio Auría...* the rest were all names of villages and rivers.

Our coffee companion comes up to us, friendly and formal, to say goodbye:

"Gentlemen, I have to get off at the next stop. I wish you both great success, and good luck with what you're doing. It has been a pleasure to share..." For a moment he is left without words; but then he resumes his speech. "I'm going to Barruelo de Santillán, a mining district. It seems that the Vizcayan firm of Altos Hornos has bought the mines there, and,

"Iglesia de Villamayor". José Caballero.

as part of the new energy policy, intends to exploit them again."

The man's name is Ángel Alonso.

"If there is any way I could help you", he says finally, pulling out a visiting card from his wallet. "This is the number where you can reach me during work hours, from eight to one thirty. And…" Leaning on the table in between the seats, he tries to write down his home number on the card, but, "without glasses I cannot see or even put a glass to my mouth."

Oslé has some advice for him:

"If you do it like that, you're only going to write badly. The trick is to stay upright without bending over."

«"Cillamayor", he says, "We've arrived". And then he takes his leave again»

Outside, the oaks are becoming scarcer. We are descending. Fields of wheat and barley begin appearing, as do adobe houses. We cross another track.

"This is a branch which comes from Aguilar and goes to Barruelo", Oslé explains.

The Hullero still has not stopped, giving our friend time for some final words of wisdom:

"This is a thought for you: make of it what you will. There's a world of difference between coming here by train, and coming in a car. Fortunately I've always been lucky enough to have travelled by train, though there was the unfortunate time when my mother died, and I had no choice in the matter, as

252

there was no other means of transport available. It's a real experience, I'm not quite sure how I can put it… The first time, it's…well, if not exactly agreeable, interesting. The second time it's agreeable. And the third time…" And now his thoughts take an altogether different turn, betraying perhaps his true feelings. "You get quite bored. Because this means of transport, compared with others we have today, is… ancient". And, thank God, he's at least right about that.

"Cillamayor", he says, "We've arrived". And then he takes his leave again.

LONELY MINES,
AND THE PALENCIAN ROMANESQUE

THIS PART OF THE SMALL district of Campóo, in between the Cordillera Cantábrica and the cold bare plateaus of La Lora, is the most desolate of all the many lands this railway crosses. The station is half a kilometre from the tiny little village of Cillamayor. The fields are eroded, beaten by the winds. The station seems fragile and insignificant, lost among the surrounding solitary expanses. The author is reminded of the station at Kalda, the subject of a tale by Kafka.

«This part of the small province of Campóo is the most desolate of all the many lands this railway crosses»

'There was a moment in my life —four years ago, already— when I worked on a small railway in the heart of Russia. I never felt as abandoned as I did then. For various reasons, which I shall not go into, I was looking at that time for a place just like that; the greater the solitude, the happier I was, and so I have now no real reason to complain... At first, I had the idea of having a little vegetable garden,

"Estación de Cillamayor"
José S. Carralero

buying a cow, and thus making myself completely self-sufficient. I had even brought with me garden tools and seeds; there was certainly no lack of land: a huge wild expanse surrounded my cabin, utterly flat, without even the slightest elevation to distract the eye. But I was too weak to dominate all that land. The land was so obstinate that it remained frozen hard even in the spring, and not even the blade of my new axe was able to penetrate it. Everything that I sowed there died.'

But the solitary expanses of Cillamayor are not like that, not at all. The village's Romanesque church, with its curious, three-windowed round apse, provides relief for pilgrims and architectural lovers. And, only a few kilometers to the north, surrounded by ancient oaks, is the village of Barruelo de Santu-llán, which is well protected by the mountains of the Sierra Brañosera. Barruelo, which gave everything to the mining industry, still awaits its reward. Of its former eleven thousand inhabitants, there now remain barely two thousand. The others, such as our courteous friend Angel Alonso, have to satisfy their longings for their homeland with fleeting visits. What is going to happen next?

And to the south, no more than ten kilometers away, is Aguilar de Campóo, a medieval marvel, full of large old houses, and emblazoned palaces, with beautifully carved eaves, perched above the Pisuerga river.

The Hullero continues its journey, and Oslé his:

"If you travelled around here by bus you'd be sick all the time. Bends, nothing but bends. Train's the only way of travelling here, eh?"

I'm interested in those coaches with the little open balconies, true relics of the old days of train travel:

"There are still some of those left; and they occasionally put on one or two of them, such as yesterday, when it was Corpus Christi."

His voice is painfully monotonous, and the only variations in his tone are when he finishes a phrase with the interrogative "eh?", or with the exclamatory "of course!"

Up in the heights are occasional dark patches of oak, but the fields are dominated by the soft, emerald hues of wheat and barley.

"What's this village called?"

"Matamorisca."

Its houses are crowded together like a flock of stone sheep to defend themselves against the worst of all their enemies: solitude. Slightly apart from them, on the top of a hill, is a Romanesque church, like the prow of a ship.

The wedding feast is over. No voice now is able to rise above the rhythmical clashing of iron. The delicacies are all gone, and those who have eaten them are curled up in their seats. The rattle of the Hullero appears to have increased the force of gravity. The train's rumbling is persistent and impossible to resist. It's difficult to keep one's eyes open. But Oslé, of course, manages to keep up his vigil, blowing volutes of smoke into the air, while looking at the surroundings as if they were his.

"There's quite some wind here, eh? And even more in Castrejón. On the roofs of Castrejón are more stones than tiles, eh? So that the wind won't blow the tiles away. And the stones are this big, eh?"

Not a single tree can be seen, as if they too had been blow away by the wind.

"The lorries that do this route have to pay a road tax."

The author's eyelids cannot bear this any more: they are closing, closing; his head is falling forwards... Then he suddenly wakes up with a jump.

"The Aguilar reservoir comes all the way here. There's a biscuit factory."

We reach Salinas. The station is missing its clock; has the wind done this? Oslé gets up and walks to the standing area at the back. The Hullero starts up. The author's forehead feels cold; his blood is rushing to his stomach to help it digest the stew. The author closes his eyes, lets his head drop... Fernando enters the coach, accompanied by Oslé. Oslé sits down, lets out another mouthful of smoke, and says:

"There are also mines here: those of San Cebrián de Mudá."

Fernando goes to the seats in the front to photograph some of the passengers. We cross a bridge.

"It's the Pisuerga", says Oslé.

The Hullero is once again following the winding path of a river, this time at an altitude of some one thousand metres, with the track flanked by mountains rising to three times that height. Oak woods cover them like a cloth that has been draped over their peaks.

A traveller approaches from the middle part of the coach. He is wearing a knitted dark red jacket embroidered above its only pocket with a type of fleur-de-lis design. Behind his thick glasses he appears to have a squint. He asks Oslé if the train is going to arrive in time at Cistierna, as he has a bus to catch. Oslé assures him that it will. But the traveller, far from being reassured, remains rooted at Oslé's side, incapable of going back to his seat. There he remains, without saying anything, as if in need of a greater reassurance which he does not know how to ask for. Oslé makes an expansive gesture, not without its hint of wickedness.

"You'll get there with hours to spare."

The traveller knits his brow, screws up his face, and —serious, and almost contrite— returns to his seat.

Oslé sucks on his cigar, breathes in, and exhales a cloud of smoke. He points to a little wood which is spread over an undulating ridge.

"... Sierra del Brezo ..."
Río S. Carralero.

"That wood over there has been completely vandalized. Holiday-makers come here in the summer, hang around with their tents for months on end, and vandalize everything."

There's something about this that affects Oslé personally. It's not just that he minds the woods being destroyed; it's that he is showing something that is his, albeit something that has belonged to him for so many years that —his or not— he no longer values it as such.

In the background, to the right, rise the grey peaks of the Sierra del Brezo, which give way to the higher mountains of the Peña Prieta.

"In Cervera, you see everything", says Oslé.

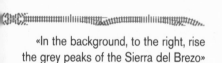

«In the background, to the right, rise the grey peaks of the Sierra del Brezo»

The station of Vado-Cervera is solitary and cold. Grass grows so abundantly between the tracks that it almost hides them. On a shunting is the broken body of a freight car, which stands on its wheels like some strange but eloquent monument to the decay of the mining industry, and the abandoning of these lands.

And the author thinks that the Hullero, which has so zealously exploited the mines of this area, has neglected the marvels that lie hidden in Palencia's wild, northern districts. Behind us, separated from us by a mountain, is Quintanaluegos, barely a scattering of noble houses, laid out along the banks of the Pi-

264

suerga, and grouped around a church whose belfry is in a style in between Romanesque and Gothic. And, three kilometres to the north of the station is the ancient and extremely beautiful town of Cervera, with its arcaded streets, balconied galleries, and traces of three medieval castles, all set in a valley that softens the severe landscape perforated by the Pisuerga.

This mountainous corner of Palencia is possibly the part of Spain richest in Romanesque churches.

The traveller with the squint returns. His fears now hang so heavily on his face that he seems drunk. Oslé does not even let him speak.

"You'll get there with hours to spare. Relax, you've got all the time in the world."

The man goes back to his seat, insecure and hesitant.

«Castrejón has a Renaissance church with a beautiful ogee window»

In between repeated snatches of sleep, the impression of travelling across high altitude plateaus has all but gone. The Hullero, in fact, has never really been anything other than a mountain train. To the north and north-east, the horizon is bordered by the grey and ragged limestone peaks leading up to the Picos de Europa; in their wake has been left every possible type of fissured, fractured, uneven terrain. The dense, dark green of oak woods alternate with sparse and springy bushes. Every so often there are bare and black-stained, porous mounds- conical rashes that have sprung up from

FRAGUAS.

the coal mines. Stones of every size cover the ground. There is broom in abundance.

We approach Castrejón. The white stones look like papers that have been scattered in the wind. But there don't appear to be any stones on the roofs. Oslé is disappointed:

"That's great, isn't it? No stones on the roofs today. But look, look! Look over there! There are definitely some there!"

Castrejón seems a small and slightly disjointed village. But among its monuments is a Renaissance church with a beautiful ogee window.

To the right, opposite the station, and on the other side of the rock that gives the place its name, is the village of Transpeña, whose parish church of the Transfiguration is a gothic treasure with wonderful pointed archivolts

And only two kilometers from Castrejón, following the path of the Hullero, is Pisón de Castrejón, where there rises another marvel —a tiny Romanesque church of the 13th century. Anyone who has just seen but once this building's stunning façade with its pointed archivolts, as delicate as birds' tongues, and its frieze in which the Saviour is flanked on both sides by gothic apostles— will always dream of returning.

PHILEAS FOGG

T HE STATION AT CASTREJÓN is now behind us. Oslé has given up on what is left of his cigar, and has
disappeared off into other parts of the Hullero.

The author is out of sorts. The hour for do-
zing has passed. He gets up,
stretches his legs, walks a few
yards. Then he encounters his
first friend on the train, the
woman who was going to Cis-

«The station at Castrejón
is now behind us»

tierna. She is in conversation with Fernando and
an elderly couple. She has introduced Fernando into
her group, as if she was testifying for his character;
and she now does the same for the author.

"This is the other gentleman", she says.

Further on, occupying a seat next to the aisle,
is the impatient passenger "with hours to spare."

I sit down beside him, on the seat next to the
window. To get there I have to climb over his feet,
which don't budge, and negotiate my way around
the knees of those in front: a woman with a green

269

"Minas de Castrejon"
Jai S. Carralero.

knitted jacket, and loose, wavy grey hair, and a girl of about twelve who's immersed in a *Tom and Jerry* comic. The woman has a knitted brow, and an evasive look; her silence is a hostile one. They are getting out at the next station, and they've begun to get ready.

The man besides me is unsociable enough to be the woman's husband, perhaps even the father of the girl. But he is not. He is speaking, but not to them. Instead he talks to a middle-aged couple sitting opposite each other, on the other side of the aisle. The couple are shy, with the look of rabbits about to run out of their burrows. But since the author's arrival, they have decided to stay put, and concentrate their glances on what can be seen from the window: a mountain covered in broom. Every so often they spy on the author, but do so only with the corner of their eyes. As soon as the author returns their look, they turn away quickly, pretending nothing has happened, yet coming away with sweet smiles. They are like angels.

In contrast, the impatient passenger is some-one without any peace or calm; he is a Lucifer. It's quite clear he doesn't like the author's proximity to him. His huge body moves restlessly on the seat like a tuna fish pulled out of water. His corpulence too has something tuna-like about it, being based not so much on the breadth of his shoulders but on the general and uniform bulkiness of his body, the great thickness of his neck and arms.

The author, in as soft a voice as the Hullero will allow, asks him:

"You're going to Cistierna, aren't you?"

But the passenger sways about, raises himself so that he can change the position of his legs, and answers "Yes!" in a way that is like an untimely punch on the face.

The author smiles, and swallows his saliva. He dares ask another question:

"You've got a connection to catch, haven't you?"

The reply is like a second punch:

"Yes!"

The woman in green and her child get off at Villaverde-Tarilonte. The station, built like that of Arija with blocks whose joins have been painted white, is missing its main sign. Is the wind once again to blame? There remains, nonetheless, one of the old pumps (looking like a lamp-post with an elephant trunk) that provided water for the boilers of the steam trains.

The Sierra de Brezo, with its rocky surface exposed to the dark sky, highlights the sense of desolation and destitution that hangs in the air.

The Hullero starts up with all its many, familiar noises, its giant's cough, its dragon's death rattle. The two angels, standing up already, with their luggage in their hands (they are getting off at the next stop), are smiling beatifically.

We approach Santibáñez de la Peña, at the foot

VILLAVERDE-TARILONT

FRAGUAS.

of El Canto Negro, where there are also mines: those of Chimbo, those of San Fidel, that of Acebal; behind us is the Peña del Fraile, which is 2,025 metres high.

"This is really beautiful, isn't it?"

And out comes the predictable reply:

"Yes!"

What is wrong with our man? The two angels, now that they are standing, seem to look at him in an even more protective way, to which he responds by raising his head, as if offering his hand.

We reach Santibáñez. The angels alight. Our man gets up, and tries to accompany them to the door.

"No, please stay seated. Don't trouble yourself. Let's hope it all works out as best as it can", they say in unison.

"Goodbye, goodbye", says the man sadly, distressed, grief-stricken. He waves his right hand, which he then immediately covers with the other one. All his fingers on that hand, except the index finger, are missing from the root upwards.

«Villaverde-Tarilonte has one of the old pumps that provided water for the boilers of the steam trains»

When the couple goes, the atmosphere outside of destitution comes in, wrapping itself around our man, and holding him tightly within its slithery grip.

The Hullero begins to move and make the sounds of a blacksmith at his forge. Our man places his fingerless hand to his throat. Insecure, hesitating, helpless, our man, seems drunk without even having had a drop to drink.

The author begins seriously to worry, and thinks it time to explain himself to him. He says he intends writing a book about the Hullero, about those who travel on it, and the landscapes it passes…

Our man becomes tamer, and says:

"Generally speaking I think that the railway is very proportionate to the mountains, and the scenery. Very proportionate, as I see it, in everything, both in the money that has been spent on it, and in its upkeep, which I don't think is bad at all, but, as I said before, proportionate to everything else, which does not mean to say, in this time when we need to save on money and energy, that too much attention has been paid to it, but rather that superfluous costs have been avoided, so as not to lead on to the greater problems arising from the urgent problems we are facing today."

«The Hullero begins to move and make the sounds of a blacksmith at his forge»

Christ almighty! The author does not know where to turn. But there's something so strangely pitiful about the man that it is difficult not to respond seriously, sadly even.

The man, contrary to initial appearances, does not have a squint. Instead his thick glasses shield myopic eyes that look at you as if from the top of a well. And, from closer by, they have a distracted

276

FKAGNAS

and vaguely absent look, expressive perhaps of some passing sorrow brought on by a momentary change in personality.

Telling him how much I agree with his opinion of the railway, I then speak admiringly of the incomparable way the track has been laid out, and how the Hullero is a true creature of the mountains.

Our man reacts unexpectedly.

"You'll have to forgive me", he says. "You'll have to forgive me", he repeats.

The author looks at him expectantly.

"Yes, yes", he says. "You must excuse me. But I'm certainly not making any sense to you, my words must seem incoherent and unconsidered. It's just that I've been very affected by... by a terrible event that has made me travel all the way from Brussels to Sahagún. A very terrible event..."

The author does not know what to say. He's stifled by distress. He knows he has no right to ask questions, and he wishes he had never spoken to the man in the first place. The man's huge body seems to him now like a wound he has opened in the coach. He now understands why the person was behaving so strangely, and why the middle-aged couple was treating him with such care and tact.

"What time is it? What time is it?", he asks, dramatically moving around in his seat.

"Four o'clock", I tell him.

"Three nephews of mine have died in an accident,

and a fourth is seriously ill in hospital, fighting for his life. I've now got to take a bus to Sahagún."

"I'm so sorry", I say.

The author is annoyed with himself for having been so initially insensitive to the man's sorrow.

"When did it happen?", I ask.

"They told me on Sunday at eleven in the morning, and, as there was no plane until nine that evening, it no longer seemed to matter when I arrived. So I took the train on Wednesday, and nine hours later —nine hours, eh?— I got from Brussels to Irún. Then it took a whole day to get to Bilbao, so I had to sleep the night there, and the following day, that's to say today, I took this train, despite everyone's misgivings, but I am very glad to have done so. I see it as very proportionate to the landscape, which gives a lot of pleasure, and I don't think anyone could disagree with that."

His journey seems certainly a strange one to have done in an emergency. The author asks him:

"And when do you intend to go back."

"It's all the same to me", the man says, "I'll take my holidays now, it doesn't matter when I return; if I take off a month, I'll be back in a month; if I take off two, I'll be back in two. It's all the same to me. My boss over there, the owner, is very understanding. Over there you work, and you resolve issues. There's always room for flexibility. It's not the same over here."

While speaking he has made a gesture with his right hand.

"Where did you lose your fingers", I ask.

"Here! Here, in Spain!", he answers, in a tone that implies, "Where else?"

In Guardo
I Found a Tasty Mouth

W<small>E REACH</small> G<small>UARDO</small>: the station has a two-coloured facade (the upper half is in exposed brick), and there's an ironwork canopy confirming its importance.

Guardo's mining wealth, none the less, is not based on coal but on anthracite, which is mined on the southern slopes of the Sierra del Brezo. A power station and a factory belonging to Río Tinto Explosives give the place an industrial appearance. And this is evident in the large railway station, with its numerous tracks, and recent renovation.

«The station has a two-coloured facade, and there's an ironwork canopy confirming its importance»

My neighbour gets up, turns towards the window, makes all the motions of looking outside, without actually looking; he then walks towards the back of the carriage, whether to go to the toilet, or to interrogate Oslé again. Who knows.

I go up to Fernando, who, from the opposite end of the carriage, is photographing its interior. In the station, indifferent to all the coming and going, a local

GUARDO

Tri S-Carralero.

beauty —a true Melina Mercouri, with thick black hair, round shoulders, and long and fulsome arms— is seated on a stone bench, whiling away her moments of leisure, her head gently tilted to one side, her stretched-out legs pressed together to form a mermaid's tail. Fernando quickly changes the direction of his camera.

The Hullero starts moving. The girl, a black swan, with a well-formed and lovely body, catches sight of us once the train is already in motion. Her look is weary, and inanimate; she stares in our direction without taking us in, almost with the same indifference towards us as the landscape. Then suddenly a change comes over her; her body, while continuing to recline like that of an indolent queen, tenses, and from her mouth protrudes a long, large and beautiful tongue —an act which has the not-so-appealing effect of wrinkling her features into an appalling grimace. Oh, women of Spain!

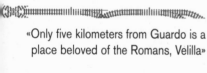

«Only five kilometers from Guardo is a place beloved of the Romans, Velilla»

A young lady similar to this one must have been the inspiration to this ditty penned by a local 14th-century rabbi, Don Sem Tob of Carrión:

I found a tasty mouth
With saliva most juicy
The sweetest thing it was
But bitter when I left it.

We go back to our respective seats. My neighbour does not return. We cross a metal bridge. A bridge over the Carrión.

We are getting closer to León. Soon we shall cross the province's border. These high Palencian valleys, with their rippling hills of oak, are but a continuation of those of our home land.

Only five kilometers from Guardo, upstream along the Carrión, is a place beloved of the Romans, Velilla. Pliny refers to its *Fontes Tamarici* as one of nature's wonders. The place in question is an intermittent spring whose waters were famed for centuries for their healing and even magical properties. One wonders what marvelous, indigenous nymphs have sported themselves in this spring whose Latin name sounds straight from an old pharmacy.

León, León

THE HULLERO enters León at the highest point of the line (1,190 metres), and stops soon afterwards in the small station of La Espina. The passenger building, isolated in the middle of a rugged countryside, seems like a solitary boat rocked by waves. Next to it is a small, rectangular watering place.

We continue. The woods get thicker. Fields spread over the ridges. There are lots of

«The mineral wealth of the area has left pathetic scars on the landscape»

cows, just as there were on leaving Vizcaya; but these ones are not white, but greyish brown. Perhaps in this respect Sabino Arana was right.

The mineral wealth of the area has left pathetic scars on the landscape. Slag heaps and black mounds —to which broom has sometimes miraculously attached itself— rise up everywhere like malignant growths. And the green of the fields, the freshness of the meadows, and the air the woods breathe, seem at the mercy of these excrescences, just like a body is when pitted by disease.

My neighbour does not come back. I slowly
make my way to the back of the coach, and, without
going through to the standing area, see him there,
leaning against the exit door. He is with a tall man
who is speaking to him.

I retrace my steps. Immediately we stop at Valcuende.

Fernando, who has not been affected for a moment by the somnolence of the siesta hour, is now slowly, almost silently bringing the passengers to life, speaking only the bare minimum, and using just his camera as his means of seduction; thus the sense of solidarity which had been forged during the lunch and its aftermath is now taking on a new dimension, with the coach beginning to appear like an excursion in which all the passengers have known each other beforehand.

An elderly couple is posing for Fernando. They've just come from spending a few days in the house of one of their children, in a village in Vizcaya. The man, a retired miner, in a black hat, suit and waistcoat, and with a chain watch, is seated with his legs apart, looking at the camera as he would Alice's looking glass, conscious of there being another world behind it. The woman has a surprisingly youthful skin, and a sweet, chirpy voice which, paradoxically, expresses a fuddy-duddy tetchiness verging on the humorous. She says:

Puente Almuhey

"Yes. We're going to have to vote for the person who's unmentionable."

And then:

"We only want them not to take away what is ours."

He, in contrast —a calm and smiling person, whose expressiveness is entirely concentrated in his eyes, with barely a movement of his facial muscles— counters the words of his wife with numerous sarcasms.

"The priest of Yungueros is quite something",

Puente Almuhey
FRAGMS.

he says, making everyone around him laugh. "When all's going well, fine; but when it's not, God help anyone who goes to see him."

She offers us a sip from a whitish liquid which she carries in a jar of Nescafé. We say no, but thank her profusely. The liquid is a quack's brew (made from some mushroom soaked in milk), whose name the author did not write down.

"It's good for everything", according to her.

A young woman, seated about two rows from where we are, comes up to say:

"Now, if you ask me about my life, you'll get something interesting", she says with a splendid smile that is echoed in the laughter of others.

The nearness of the journey's end, and the prospect of returning to the dearly missed homeland, seems to have aroused a general optimism and euphoria.

The author, not wishing to disappoint the young woman, goes up to her on the train's arrival at Puente Almuhey. She is called Valeria. She's travelling with her husband. They're both from Yungeros. They're going to a wedding which is going to be held in León on the Saturday.

"Will this get on the telly?", Valeria asks the author.

When I explain what in fact we're doing, the formerly lively Valeria clams up. At times she laughs a bit (slightly soullessly), while the nearby passengers, still hoping for her to regale us with funny remarks, try and eavesdrop. But she has a curious sense of propriety that prefers her husband to do now all the talking. And he does so in a ponderous manner.

He is dark, strong, and swarthy, and with a flat neck; he used to wrestle, and you can tell. With his bare hands he could tear apart the Madrid telephone directory. He works for Bilbao's suburban railways, and his company's identity card is written in Basque and Spanish. He says:

"Anyone today who wants to work where I do needs to speak Basque. Those already employed are recommended to spend an hour a day learning the language. The company will pay half your class fees; the employee has to pay the other half."

"Oh, if only there was work in León!", she then says.

"Would you go back there?"

"In a jiffy", they both answer.

THE SLEEPING BEAUTY
AND *PASSE-PARTOUT*

IN FRONT OF THE AUTHOR, though on the other side of the aisle, is a young and beautiful woman, in trousers and polo neck jersey, and with a scarf tied over her head in the country fashion. Not so long before she had been laughing at Valeria's comments; but now she is feigning a deep and peaceful sleep.

She's travelling on the end seat, the only seat in the coach that's on its own: there's no seat facing hers; and the space across the aisle normally occupied by the twin seats, is taken up by the toilet. Hers is seat number one; the author's is number four.

«A young and beautiful woman, in trousers and polo neck jersey, and with a scarf tied over her head»

With her eyes closed, her face clean and smooth, and her hair hidden behind the handkerchief, she is a most attractive sight. Her full, red lips highlight the whiteness of her skin. Every so often she opens her large, dark eyes, and stares out fixedly, defiantly, not wholly seriously; then she pretends once more to be asleep.

The author watches her spellbound, and regrets not having any of the fairy tale prince's resources to wake the *Sleeping Beauty*. He gets up, approaches her, and then, when he is right beside her, does not dare to break the spell. The author then remembers the impatient passenger from Brussels, and walks through the door to where the man had been standing. The man is still there. The passenger who is with him is tall and dark, with a suede jacket, and a green tie. He is speaking with great fluency. The two men look at the author. The impatient passenger seems completely worn out. The author turns towards the window as if to watch the countryside. The other man, far from interrupting his speech, raises the already pretentious tone of his voice, and continues saying:

"I'm looking for a doctrine which does not believe in original sin. Marxism, just like Christianity believes in original sin. How else can it justify otherwise the concept of capital gain? Capital gain, here, as in Brussels, or China, or anywhere else for that matter, is the additional economic benefit which the work of the salaried man gains for the person employing him, once the salary has been deducted. But capital gain is also the interest earned by that other factor in the production chain: capital good. Only by accepting the basic illegality of property, that is to say original sin, can you deny to the employer this sum that is owed him."

The author, dumbfounded, now takes a look

inside the coach, as if to assure himself that everything there is still in order. We have arrived at Prado de la Guzpeña, and *Sleeping Beauty* is getting up. She is having difficulties in taking her luggage down from the rack. The author enjoys a spot of wrestling as he rushes to help her.

I'm standing right next to her, in such a way that I can also see the two men on the other side of the door. I'm worried that the impatient man is about to faint.

Sleeping Beauty sits down again, but only for a moment. The spell is broken once and for all. She bends over her travelling case, which is now on the floor, and takes out a hair brush of scary dimensions. She stands up nimbly, like a bird taking flight, and bravely removes her headscarf, letting her long and soft brown hair fall down over her back and shoulders. Leaning to one side she starts combing her hair; then she leans in the opposite direction, and combs the other side, doing so with passion, energy, fury… God, what a woman!

"At least they'll see me looking at my best", she says.

Sleeping Beauty tells me she's from the Lois area, to where she is now going. She does not smile, but instead welcomes the conversation in an almost compulsive way, as if shaking of all the many stretches of the journey she has passed in silence. When she speaks, there's no stopping her.

The ring she wears is only an engagement ring. She's a nurse in Bilbao, and her fiancé works in the same hospital. They've been together for three and a half years. Her fiancé is from La Linea de la Concepción.

"I was there last year, and I liked it a lot'. But now I wouldn't change León for anything in the world. I've already said that to my fiancé. Look, I said, I'm just a stubborn oaf. And if I get it into my head to do so, I'll come back here, and everyone can say what they want."

Behind us, the Brussels man has let his forehead slump against the window. The other man does not stop talking. Nor does *Sleeping Beauty*:

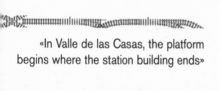

«In Valle de las Casas, the platform begins where the station building ends»

"How am I going to sleep, with all this upping and downing, bending and turning, backing and forwarding. This shitty train, if you'll excuse me, doesn't seem to avoid a single stone. It's just not for me, this rubbishy old thing. But the problem is I'm always wanting to go home, I do so whenever I can… Now, I've got permission to stay away until Tuesday. But it's just not made for me, this. I can never find a comfortable position. My bum's… It's also such a long journey, I only like short ones. The trouble is if I take the other line, the connections aren't so good. I'd get to León at twelve, and would have to wait until eight in the morning before taking the bus."

Valle de las casas
FRAGUAS

We reach the stop of Valle de las Casas. Surprisingly, the platform begins where the station building ends. The impatient traveller enters the coach once more. The author and *Sleeping Beauty* tuck themselves in so that he can get past. The other passenger is behind him. He's tall, with a drawn face; his hair is very dark, receding quickly, and covered in dandruff; and he has a big, hairy moustache that is like a black bush. He's still speaking:

"And though I say so myself, I'm a revolutionary in everything except biology. No, when it comes to that, I'm not. I wouldn't go that far."

When he passes me he pauses. He gives me a knowing wink, and smiles. His smile is barely noticeable, little more than a glow in his eyes, a wrinkle at the corner of his mouth. It's a strange, self-satisfied smile, like that of someone constantly amused within himself. He whispers to me:

"He's got to be distracted."

Sleeping Beauty says:

"My father is Basque. I'm as well; I was born in Bilbao, but there's nowhere like Lois. There are lots of young people who live in Lois, mainly working on the land. There's also the odd Basque. There's a man from Bilbao who's made for himself an enormous mill. He's married, and lives with his wife. But he also brings there his secretary, and Christ knows what other women. This man's… ETA is looking for him. he lives in the mill, and few people know him, because the place is quite out of the way."

The impatient passenger has sat down. I would have liked to say goodbye to him. But Sleeping Beauty, whose greatest asset was her feigned sleep, does not let me.

We are going downhill.

Unusually for a person so young, *Sleeping Beauty* reveals when awake a relentless gift of the gab:

"My father is Basque. My parents are Basque. But

300

when they bury me, it's Lois. We were born in Bilbao, but when we were children we were raised in Lois. I wouldn't change Lois for nowhere in the world. In December, and during my holidays, it's always Lois for me."

There'll be no-one from her family waiting for her in the station, so she'll have to take a bus to Lois.

"But I'll give a call beforehand, to say that I'm okay. Because so many things have happened here in the past. The last time I took the train, we were derailed. And another time, about three months ago, a woman died. In December, when we all came, we were also derailed. Every time the train speeds up I die from fear… Thank goodness my parents were with me the first time we got derailed. God, that was scary! Then I've been derailed several times on my own. God, was I frightened! All that rocking about, one day we're going to fall right over."

The Esla appears to the left; its dark waters contrast with the grey rocks. The train is climbing, the Esla is descending, making its way towards where all the waters of León are aiming. The horizon is opening up, pushing away the brown and ochre hillsides. Poplars and wooden fences dot the expanding fertile plain.

When in Cistierna,
Ask to Speak to the Director

W E REACH CISTIERNA. The coach clears out.
The impatient traveller gets off, as do *Sleeping Beauty*,
and our first friend from the train, the one who lived
in Eíbar...

"Nice meeting you, have
a good journey!", she tells us.

We get down as well. The
station of Cistierna is a vital
stop on the line, and has all the

«The station of Cistierna is a vital
stop on the line, and has all the signs
of being so»

signs of being so. Its main building has the statutory
canopy, but in wood this time, and —unusually—
sloping upwards.

Cistierna, like Valmaseda, has a long railway
history, and has been a major junction for years.
The town is at edge of the great fertile valley which
has been opened up by the Esla (the king of León's
rivers, the ancient Astura of legendary fame) right
under the shadow of the Peña Corada, a colossus 1,835
metres high.

León's suburban trains run as far as Cistierna, just

«Estación de Cistierna»

Luis S. Carretero

as Bilbao's go to Valmaseda. And, as with the latter, Cistierna is also a depot for locomotives. The warehouse building, in a sad state of repair ever since most of the steam trains were taken out of service, is a stone building with a pitched roof, and arched doors.

Now that the beautiful village of Riaño is threatened by being submerged under a reservoir, Cistierna has become the capital of the mountainous district of the Esla. And if that ridiculous threat comes off, Cistierna will be the main town of a district extending deep into the heart of the impressive Picos de Europa, those calcareous giants whose imposing peak of Peña Santa (2.596 metres) commands majestic views towards the Asturian sea and the fair meadows flanking the rivers of León.

«The warehouse building has been in a sad state of repair ever since most of the steam trains were taken out of service»

Steam trains —destined eventually for the power-stations of La Robla or Guardo— still run to Cistierna along the Hulleras de Sabero branch line, carrying coal from the mines of Sabero. These mines, the most important within the Hullero's orbit, lie only ten kilometres upstream from here, along the Esla.

This branch line is the same width as ours, and has to negotiate the Esla on a metal bridge forty-five metres long.

We walk back towards the engine car. A railway inspector is talking to Chuchi from the platform. Chuchi warns us:

cisterna
loi*l-Canolew

"You're going to have to show him your letter before getting on."

I take out the envelope from my pocket, extract the letter from the director general of the FEVE, Don Mariano Pascual, and show it to the inspector. He reads it carefully. Chuchi says:

"It's signed by Pascual."

Everything's in order, and we climb on board.

The Hullero sets off again.

"Have you eaten?", asks Chuchi.

We say we have.

"Do you want any wine?", he asks, offering us an almost full bottle of red. We have a drink. Chuchi says:

"Wine doesn't agree with…What's it like?"

"Very good. Do you want a sweet?"

Chuchi, delighted, takes one, saying, as he unwraps it:

"I've got all this meat left." Then he points to his pot, which lies discarded on the floor.

We cross the Esla on a stone bridge eighty-five metres long, almost the same length as the one over the Ebro. Then, after doing an almost complete turn, follow the river downstream.

"I also have a letter from Pascual", says Chuchi. "They gave me eighteen thousand pesetas for having avoided a crash."

Then, after a pause, he fires off three questions at ridiculous speed:

"Is he old yet, Pascual? Is he still in Madrid? Did he give you a letter each?"

These are questions that are as much expressions of curiosity as they are ones of astonishment that an important part of his fate should be controlled by someone so far away.

"Are you going to see him afterwards? Tell him that there's this driver, Mr. So-and-So, Jesús Gutié-rrez Artuaga, alias 'Chuchi', who's going to retire in two years time, on October 1st, and that he'll have spent between forty and forty-three years in the service. Tell him that."

The Esla runs winding and slaty.

"Let's see if they give him a tip, because that's what Pascual does."

Chuchi's eyes, of indeterminate colour, some-times blue, sometimes green, have acquired a fine, glassy layer, like a solid tear.

The Esla heads off south, while the Hullero skirts a mountain to the north-east.

We start climbing again.

"This journey's heavy going", says Chuchi.

"It certainly is", I say, "I'm getting incredibly tired."

"Of course, now it's summer, it's pretty, isn't it? Do you want to sit down?"

"Absolutely not", I say, "but thanks."

But he has already set up the folded seat, and I'm forced to sit. His ardent desire to please is stronger than his huge hand over my shoulder. Now, more than ever, the cabin seems to be suffocating him. And, just like a chained man, he stands with his legs apart so that his fetters won't grate against him.

"Now if this were the other engine car you'd be able to sit all the time. But this one's better for looking at the track."

His comments give me an excuse to get up. An oak wood flanks one side of the train.

Chuchi has changed. Since leaving him on his own at Berceo, the intervening six hours of solitude and tiredness seem clearly to have affected him. Thoughts, funny stories, and songs, must have been simmering away inside him just like the meat in the pot. And now they're all coming out, in an endless stream.

"There was this miller once in Valmaseda, and there were lots of Carlists and Liberals around; and he used to sing: 'Look how they run, pom titty pom, look how they run, pom titty pom'."

He brings his arms together, and simulates pistol shots by striking the middle finger of his right hand against the base of the index finger. Bang! Bang!

"He used to imitate a snake and say: 'Look at the snake, it's biting you, it's eating you up.' Bang! Bang!"

The festive mood that has now taken over Chuchi goes well with the red flower tucked behind his ear.

"Where did you get that flower?"

"In León."

And he shows me three flowers, small and withered: two red ones and an orange one, all lost amidst the chaos of papers, bags and rags that he carries on the metal instrument panel.

"And if you don't bring any flowers, you don't do the journey?"

"That's right! They're from San Roque, Salamanca, El Viti, whose a relative of mine, I always tell them". Then immediately, he adds: "That's a lie, you know."

"Do you like bull-fighting?"

"Of course! I've been a bull-fighter in my time. No longer. And I've gone bike racing with Barrendero and someone else, who was killed, Pepe Somebody-or-Other; and then there were Luis, Esteban, Trueba. Trueba was on the television the other day. I can't remember that other person's name, they killed him. Do you want some more wine?"

Chuchi hands over the bottle in such a way that it's impossible to refuse. He doesn't join us.

"There's not the same enthusiasm any more for cycling. Nor for playing pelota. I had a brother who was killed in the Civil War; he was a brilliant player. The other brother was left crippled. The war fucked up all the youth around here. And now? Now there's no respect for anyone. Before we were more… Now, they're killing the whole human race. Now they just kill anyone, you can't just kill anyone.

The government's to blame. They're killing the police. You can't just go round killing people like that. I don't know if they're from the right, or from the left, or if they're from ETA, or Fuerza Nueva, they're all the same, aren't they? At the end of the day they're killing young and old alike. And those doing it will have to pay for it in the end, won't they?"

We continue climbing. The Hullero is snoring like a live animal, but, paradoxically, after its long journey, it seems faster; its pace is cheerful, animated, and nervous; as nervous and animated as Chuchi himself.

MEMORIES OF THE HULLERO

W E REACH YUGUEROS. It's just after five thirty. Yugueros is a hamlet with little more than half a dozen houses, a few farms and a Romanesque church, which crowns a hill to the right of the track, and is a tumbledown but (for something so humble) beautiful structure, whose tower asserts itself above the rest of the building, and even seems to puff out its chest when the Hullero passes by.

«Yugueros is a hamlet with little more than half a dozen houses, a few farms and a Romanesque church»

The connecting of Yugueros with the rest of the world is another of the not insignificant achievements of the Hullero, because, apart from the railway, there is only a steep cow track linking the hamlet in winter with Cistierna.

The station master blows his whistle. Chuchi pulls the engine's.

"Let's go", he says.

Chuchi is happy, and the Hullero even more so. After so many days of doing exactly the same

313

Yagueros
Prague

route, the train surely knows that it's about to arrive,
and that its journey from now onwards is going to
be like the last metres of the exhausted steed who
begins to sense the sweet smells of the stable.

"There are lots of cows around here, aren't there?",
says Chuchi. "And lots of mushrooms, eh? It's cold.
Should I shut the window?"

"No, it's fine, it's fine."

Young poplars, wide in girth, and close together, turn the sides of the railway bank into walls of green.

We're now going down. Chuchi strokes the engine with his piece of steel wool.

"It's not easy going downhill. I've got to go down a couple of notches."

Some greyish brown cows are grazing on the gentle slopes. There's a sign in the railway bank telling drivers to whistle. Chuchi pulls on the cable. Cows lift up their heads and twist their necks in the direction of the Hullero. These are their only movements.

La Ercina. The coal from the mines of Casetas used to be brought here along the Oceja gorge on one of the tiny trains that were once so plentiful in this area. From here most of the coal was taken to La Robla.

«Some greyish brown cows are grazing on the gentle slopes»

To this day the station still keeps its coal-loading platform, as well as a circular water tower —two features that no longer serve any purpose.

"There used to be many unexploited mines here", says Chuchi. "Why did they give up on them?"

But Chuchi is still in the same high spirits.

"Come on, drink some wine", he tells us.

He unwraps another sweet, and put it in his mouth. His driving, always done standing up, with his back bent over the controls, seems now more exhausting than ever.

317

"If I stretch out to my full height, I'm always hitting myself in the chest. When a small bloke comes up to me", he says, pointing to the author, who's one hundred and seventy five centimetres tall, "I tell him you can't hear a bloody thing from my height, and that he's going to have to spend the night chatting to my bum. To others I say that they're going to have to bury me twice when they take me to the cemetery: once here, and the second time in the church."

Chuchi brakes, and the Hullero snorts. But the Hullero is happy as it descends. The imminent prospect of the journey's end seems to make it happier with each passing kilometre. And Chuchi expresses its pleasure with a strange loquacity.

"There was once this driver on this line —the chap died before the war— who used work with train Sixteen. How's it going mate? He used to say. Very well, thank you. The priest is well too, but he's missing an arm. Then he used to say: rob and kill as much as you want, but never meddle in other people's affairs."

He brakes:

"Oh, he was a naughty old bugger, he was!"

He brakes:

"Christ, he was a naughty old bugger!"

Chuchi seems now to occupy more of the engine car than ever. And yet, though fatigue shows all over his enormous body, it does not seem to hold him back, but has rather the opposite effect, and speeds up and amplifies his gestures and movements. He needs to renew his steel wool, and pulls out a clean piece from a plastic bag. But before doing so, he has to push aside my notebook.

"I'm sorry", I say, "I'm in your way, aren't I?"

"Not in the slightest", he answers, "In fact you're doing me a favour, you're keeping me company. And just imagine if anything happened to me when I was on my own. This job is for young chaps this is, not old farts such as me, I'm too bloody old. I'm going to be sixty, sixty! Can you bloody believe it?"

His voice is like a shout, without modulations, powerful, and difficult to understand.

"I spent the war carrying heavy artillery in the mountains of Vitoria, with a mule and a horse. That was some bloody work, I can tell you! I was given some tube sized ten and a half, which weighed God knows how many kilos, and I had to drag it on my own. If I had to do the same today, I'd probably end up killing everyone."

While speaking he strains to talk louder, but the sweet in his mouth makes this even more difficult. It seems he's missing all his lower teeth but one, which is bent and long and crosses his tongue like a sabre. When he speaks, this tooth, isolated and lonely, shipwrecked in his mouth, rises up like a piano key when the finger releases its pressure.

"I've left all my false teeth at home, the ones I should be wearing now. I don't have them any more, they hurt me. They've done so for over a year. How they hurt! I didn't realize how much false teeth would hurt!"

He brakes. But his happiness does not go away.

"Come on. Have another drop of wine."

He continues without drinking. And he continues talking without stopping:

"This engine. I've been with it now at least seven years. I like it the most, it's my favourite. It's turned over on me twice now. The wheels were like this, shooting up into the air, and it gave me a lump this big, and left me with this arm like this over there in that corner. We were climbing: ta... ta... ta... ta... pruuuuuuuum!... and then it fell. It was completely wet, and it was left like this". He grimaces and extends his enormous arms diagonally. "Fuck that, I said. The whole bloody stew was all over the place. I lost my glasses. I lost a watch."

He brakes.

"And what happened then?"

"Fuck all. The engine didn't come off."

"What do you mean, didn't come off?"

"It didn't come off from the coaches! It was pulling two coaches, and there was the same guard who's come today". Then, as if thinking out loud, he adds: "I love this engine, I really do. They're always asking me. Aren't you afraid? Of course not. If the track doesn't come off, she's not going to either. The other engine, the yellow one, is a fucking brilliant piece of machinery. But I prefer this one any day, and if it were in a better state, it would go faster too. Many engines that have come through here have been all cleaned up and don't make any noise. But when they get here they just haven't got the strength. Because there just isn't the know-how any more. And each piece of an engine like this one is worth than a whole new engine. That's why I always tell this engineer chap, this Asturian: "Haven't you just got a good blow torch?" Because that's really the only solution. That's what's happened to them all, from numbers Fifty one to Sixty, bang, bang, bang, all to the scrapheap. That's the best thing for them really."

The railway ditch follows the straight line of a watercourse, and the Hullero breaks into a gallop, happier than ever, as if stimulated by Chuchi's words. If Oslé was a coachman in the driver's seat, Chuchi is like the impetuous postillion who rides on his front horse.

"From here onwards it's all uphill, up to La Losilla. Then it's flatter until Boñar; then it's all uphill until La Vecilla, and then it's down again."

To the left, behind a thick wall of poplars, you can glimpse the imposing stone bulk of a church, or a palace, or a convent. On the other side, to the north, the dark forms of mountains stand out under a grey sky. It's June, and yet there seems a threat of snow in the air.

At Barrillos a group of twelve boys in blue uniforms await the Hullero's arrival. Two of them are wearing stripes. They seem to be soldiers of the railway.

From Barrillos to La Losilla the Hullero glides like a worm alongside the path of a stream. For a good part of the way the landscape is sombre and lonely. Poplars, spread out by the high winds, take possession of the watercourses. Broom and pastures cover the mountain.

"A steam train", says Chuchi, "was gorgeous, wasn't it? This seems though like a funeral, eh? Tacatá, tacatá, tacatá. Just the smoke alone was wonderful. It made you happy just seeing it, it did. Tacatá, tacatá, tacatá. There were these American trains, running on dry steam: tratratrá, tratratrá, tratratrá. I had one for twenty five years. What memories I have of her! The problem is that steam trains need a lot of work, and looking after. Adjusting the connecting rods, cleaning the wheels; it was far worse than this. But they were gorgeous, they were. Tratratrá, tratratrá, tratratrá tratratrá. Oh, what memories!"

«"A steam train. Tacatá, tacatá. Just the smoke alone was wonderful"»

The author listens enthralled. He feels that the Hullero's own thoughts —impetuous, exultant, rash and tender— are all bubbling around him. And since the heart is the source of all thoughts, according

José I. Carralero.

to the ancients, then the Hullero's own heart, the author now realizes, is beating in Chuchi himself.

"Whenever I see a steam train I just stand there like an idiot. The place where you can still find steam trains now is Ponferrada. There are three of them there belonging to the Basque railways. One of them was the Fifty Euskadi, the other the Fifty-One Luria; the other, the Fifty-Six Elgolbera. Do you know them? —the Ponferrada driver asks me. Know them? I say. How can I not know them! I bloody drove them! As soon as I see them, I can immediately tell you their number and all. They look the same, but you can tell the differences."

FROM BOÑAR TO LA VECILLA

Pastures and vegetable gardens —broad,
beautiful, and surprisingly flat— abound in the valleys
of Boñar. These rich lands, so fertile in appearance,
are dotted with poplars, and crisscrossed with hedges
and paths, gardens and sown
fields.

«Vegetable gardens, broad, beautiful,
and surprisingly flat»

At the station of Boñar,
thirty people, mainly men, are
waiting under the ironwork
canopy. The two storied building, is grey with a
white border around the façade and windows. At
the end of the platform, near a round watering place,
there's a picturesque outbuilding. Its red pitched
roof projects widely like an excessively broad beret.
Next to the door is a discreet wall striped white and
red like the barriers in a bull-ring: it's the urinal.

The station is not unimportant; a daily train links
it to León.

We continue, and arrive soon at Porma river,
where we cross a bridge made out of masonry. Its banks

Pastizales de Boñar...
Mont. Canalon.

are shaded and luxuriant, reeds crowd together at the water's edge, and, in the background, are mountains that —before the construction of the reservoir— were once all that were needed to sustain the force of the torrent.

"Chuchi, what's your address so we can send you some photos?"

"The address of my house?"

"Yes, of your house."

"…mmm…, mmm…", he struggles, knits his brow, and eventually gives up, "I really don't remember. No, I don't. It doesn't matter, you can always get me at Valmaseda, which is better. That's where my mother is, it'll be better really."

He gives us the mother's details, which I write down in my note book.

«At the end of the platform, there's a picturesque outbuilding: it's the urinal»

"And then we'll meet up", he says.

After a while, he adds:

"I don't remember the street, I really don't. It's got some strange name. Now the street where I was born, I remember that", He tells it to us, then asks. "Is this all going down in some report?"

I explain once more the purpose of our journey, which is nothing more than the writing of a book.

"Yes, yes…", he says, nodding his head very noticeably, and with air escaping between his teeth after each monosyllable, as if he were whistling.

The Hullero is now struggling between the spurs of a magnificent mountain range preceding the Sierra de León. The ditch is plowing its way through arable fields boxed in between high pastures and oak woods. With his steel wool Chuchi wipes away the sweat from the Hullero's labours. For José María Quadrado these southern spurs of the Cordillera Cantábrica, in between Asturias and León, though not as steep or deep as those overlooking the heartland of León, have very similar characteristics. Our train is a privileged witness to this.

Chuchi says:

"We keep on climbing until those black trees. Then it's downhill, and then downhill again once we're in La Vecilla, and then it's uphill again."

Fernando asks if he can close the window.

"Close it, don't mind about me."

"Aren't we bothering you?", Fernando persists.

"Not at all! Far from it, you're keeping me company. I always like to have someone with me. So that you can do some singing and dancing. A person on his own gets bored. I've got to speak to Pascual face to face and tell him honestly what I think. A person has no right to do this on his own. If anything happens to me, the slightest thing, what then? They've got to put some heating here in the winter". He swivels round to open a door behind him. We cringe. From the open door come some of the Hullero's most appalling howls: a noise that is ferocious and deafening. "You've got to keep moving, over here, over there, up and down", he says swaying his arms all over the place with a strange, harmless fury. "I've got to see Pascual. There are over a million unemployed here in Spain, and that's serious that is. And something's got to be done about it, something really has. I can't do anything myself, because I'm going, I've got to go. After forty-three years, it's time. Even though these years mean nothing because I was with the nationalists. And if I'd been with the Reds! Oh fuck it! It's not right I should be on my own. What bloody difference whether I was with one side or the other."

The author's heart seems like a squeezed lemon. Fernando stops taking photos and is also all ears. Chuchi's giant hand, always clinging to the steel wool, makes abrupt jumps all over the instruments panel.

"There was this driver who's retired now, he used to be a stoker, and then they promoted him to driver, and it wasn't worth it for him, it wasn't bloody worth it! It's not right, I tell you, it's not bloody right. And I was with the Reds too… I've told that now to everyone. With the Nationalists I was a corporal; with the Reds I was just an ordinary soldier. They made me a corporal thanks to Article Twenty Nine."

"And what's that?"

"I don't know really", he says with an almost angelic tone and manner that are in sharp contrast to his previous mood.

"Where were you?"

"In the Ebro. On the whole of the Tortosa front; in Gandesa, and all up there, the Segre reservoir and up there, Belchite, Aragón, Cataluña, Lérida, Gerona, Tarragona, up there by the sea. And what's that called, up there, next to the Ebro? That was really pretty, that was."

Chuchi pulls the reins, and the Hullero snorts and seems almost to bend its head. In the railway bank are the most beautiful honeysuckles we've seen in the whole journey: tall, large, and vividly coloured.

Chuchi thinks we need another sip of wine. He bends over, picks up the bottle from the floor, and offers it to us with his enormously strong arm.

We refuse. He's the one who drinks this time. He says:

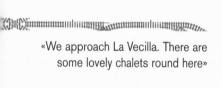

«We approach La Vecilla. There are some lovely chalets round here»

"Up there, in the Valdepeñas area, there was this wine…"

We reach a broad and very enticing flat stretch of grass. Herds of cows dot the meadows and hillsides.

"Oh, just look at the cattle over there!", says Chuchi, then adding immediately, "There's a road over there that goes to Figaredo in Asturias". And he points towards a row of hills over which rise a nearby group of mountain peaks, white and grey, knife-sharp and glistening.

We go over a stone bridge across a river that's skipping and singing, with crystalline waters that polish the stones from the mountains. The river is

La Vecilla
FRAGUAS

332

known to Chuchi and the Hullero. It's called the
Curueño:

"This is a great place for fishing", says Chuchi.

Dead trunks are piled up in the sawmills, displaying round, white wounds that are still fresh.

"There are some lovely chalets round here".

We approach La Vecilla. The whining of the Hullero seems like that of a thoroughbred whose bridle has been pulled by the rider. Steam issues ferociously from its nostrils, and the passengers waiting on the platform move aside, fearful of the strength of the irons and hoofs. Among those waiting are some soldiers and climbers (there's a confusion of rucksacks and canvas bags), the odd family with children, and a solitary, blond mountaineer, wearing shorts, and seated on a stone bench —he's the only one who does not move, or barely even breathes, at the approach of the Hullero.

«The train stops on top of a bridge spanning the main road»

"There are some really pretty chalets here", says Chuchi. "The area's beautiful. Many people spend their summers here. Lots come from Asturias."

The train stops on top of a bridge spanning the main road Nearby, on the right, is the Bar Orejas, where there once gathered those players from Cultural Leonesa —Miche, Gayo, Chas and Vallejo— who brought their team into the First Division.

The departure from La Vecilla is euphoric. The stationmaster raises the flag. Fernando gives the order: "Let's go!", he says. Chuchi applies the spurs, and the Hullero jumps forward: one two, three, then it

334

La Vecilla
FRAGUAS.

becomes irritated, hesitates, until finally it slows its pace.

The fertile landscape around us is truly beautiful, and Chuchi enthuses:

"This whole branch line is lovely now: it's full of chalets."

"What do you mean, branch line?"

"The one from Matallana to León. Before the train only went from Bilbao to La Robla, and then they built this branch line to León. The money must have come from the Bank of Bilbao and Vizcaya. And, for all I know, the government as well, with the help of the grandfather of that man."

The Hullero whistles.

"The grandfather of what man?"

"Alfonso XIII, the grandfather of Juan Carlos."

All the euphoria is not just due to the journey's approaching end: it's also inspired by the beauty of the moist green fields, and the ubiquitous, amiable presence of cattle.

"Servando is from around here", says Chuchi. "Do you know him? He's the boss in charge of us."

"No."

"Haven't you heard anyone mention him?"

"We heard something from Nazario. What's his surname?"

"I don't know his full name. We can ask in León."

Chuchi remains standing, with his bent back,

and his right hand with the steel wool leaning on the engine. It's already been more than eight hours in the same position since Valmaseda."

"I always travel like this. If my hand gets tired I change to the other one. I stand up properly to eat. And I stand up like that at other times. I get up to dance an Aragonese jig, or a Basque one." He lifts up his arms, which touch the ceiling. "You have a much better time here if there are two or three of you. That's why I wanted you two up here. You get bored on your own. I like talking… there's nothing I like more than a good natter…"

We keep on climbing. Chuchi says:

"This is the last climb, and then it's all flat". He wipes his steel wool over the engine, then adds, "This train's always climbing."

MEMORIES OF THE WAR

W E START GOING DOWNHILL.

"This where Servando comes from, that village over there. We'll ask about out his full name later."

A dozen or so little houses spill out into the landscape, following the line of an almost black row of poplars. The clouds attach themselves to the grey peaks in the background.

«The clouds attach themselves to the grey peaks in the background»

We reach the stop of Aviados.

A woman walks on the side of the railway bank, carrying what seems like a shopping bag, from which peek out some yellow flowers.

"Look at those beautiful flowers", says Chuchi.

"Dalias", says Fernando. "Let's go!"

Honeysuckle continues to decorate the sides of the railway bank. Plowed fields alternate with vegetable gardens. The oaks are stunted, and are fewer and far between; the poplars and the little black trees are laid out in rows.

"It's downhill all the way to Matallana", says Chuchi.

Chuchi brakes the Hullero. Time and time again, with great care. The Hullero puffs.

"Here, during the war", he says. "Two American engines crashed. The rails had been taken up, so they were derailed."

It's almost impossible to understand him. Added to the normal din of the machinery, and the endless groan of the engine, are now the Hullero's snorts as it descends.

"They removed the track. Two engines were coming from La Robla. And they didn't kill the people; the only one they killed was the stoker."

"But who removed the track?"

"The militiamen! Two American locomotives were coming loaded with cargo. It happened just here!"

The Hullero wiggles as it follows the level curve of a hill. We're having such difficulties in hearing Chuchi, we are paying so much attention to what he is saying, that it almost seems as if we are attempting to decipher the difficult, un-modulated voice —something in between a howl and a screech, a roar and a rumble— of the Hullero itself.

"They were going to La Robla. They were coming from Cistierna, and they landed with their wheels in the air. The stoker fell underneath the tender. He was all cut here", he says, crossing his enormous arm over his stomach. "They killed him because there was no way he was going to recover. They didn't do anything to the others. There were a couple of stokers, two guards, two drivers, and two policemen. They didn't do anything to them."

"That's extraordinary!"

"They released them immediately. They were brought to Asturias, and, four days later, they were happily walking around Vizcaya. The only one they killed was the stoker. He was shouting terrified. Ay, ay, ay! Rather than make him suffer, they killed him."

The Hullero whistles.

"This is the stop of La Valcueva", says Chuchi. "The next one is already Matallana."

"Durruti was in Matallana, Durruti, you know, the anarchist leader who had all of Catalonia at his feet. Did you realize he was from León?"

"It's all the same to me!", he shouts. "And it goes like this. Bang! Bang!" Placing the index finger of his left hand in between the small finger and index finger of his right one, he claps his palm against the base of the thumb, and sings. "How they ran, pom titty pom. How they ran, pom titty pom." Then, he says once more. "They were Carlists and Liberals."

At Valcueva two old mining railways join up, two small branch lines that have now been abandoned: one comes from the mine of La Carmonda, and the other from that of La Valenciana. Chuchi becomes indignant:

"They just haven't the right, they really haven't. They could exploit the mines, and there would be work for everyone. And now there are over a million people unemployed. I just don't understand it. Felipe González wants people to retire at sixty, and Suárez doesn't want to retire at all. Let's give youth a chance. They're paying me two salaries, and with just one of these you could employ three young people. Pascual himself has said so. He made himself very clear to the mayor of Espinosa. With one of those salaries we can pay three youths."

We approach Matallana. The Hullero snorts and puffs. Chuchi brakes it, restrains it, and calms it down.

«"This is the stop of La Valcueva. The next one is already Matallana"»

The station seems an important one. It has two platforms and three tracks. The passenger building, which is separate from the one for cargo, is very attractive, with a roof pitched on four sides and brick decorations on the façade, not to mention of course the statutory ironwork canopy. From here there are two freight trains going to La Robla, and two passenger ones to León.

"Do we stop here long?", we ask.

"Yes. We've got to put those on. We'll have to do some manoeuvres", says Chuchi, referring to three carriages on another track."

344

"We'll get off then."

"Are you getting off?", he asks in an almost agonized tone of voice.

"Then we'll get back on again."

"You'll be coming back, eh?", he says, looking down towards us. His eyes are glowing. "You'll be able to see the branch line from here. You'll be coming back, won't you?", he repeats in a begging tone.

We run around a bit to stretch our legs. In the mail coach are two men working against the clock, one in front of the other. There are few passengers on the train.

The Hullero whistles with exceptional persistence.

We go back. Chuchi, leaning almost entirely out of the window, is waving frantically at us. There aren't going to be any manoeuvres.

«The station seems an important one. It has two platforms and three tracks»

348

Pardavé, Pedrún, Matueca

WE CONTINUE. IMMEDIATELY we cross the To-río, which is deep and narrow here, bordered by great bursts of reeds, above which rises a magnificent poplar.

The Hullero changes direction. Up to now we have been crossing the foothills of the Cordillera Cantábrica, without going too far from the range's magnificent peaks. Now the train is rushing headlong like a torrent, advancing like a river, gallop-ing like a steed towards León.

«The Cordillera breaks up into rows of hills, into gentle, long watercourses»

The Cordillera breaks up into rows of hills, into gentle, long watercourses; the Hullero takes into account the way the rivers run. And, through following the Torío, just as it had followed the Cadagua on leaving Vizcaya, it finds the shortest route between the Cor-dillera Cantábrica and the city of León. The ridges, hills, and hillocks —dotted with oak and black poplars, lit up by the fluorescent yellow of broom— smoothen

the Hullero's descent, and subtly prepare it for the arrival at the great plateaus of Castile.

"There' good irrigation around here", says Chuchi.

We pass without stopping the station at Pardavé.

"There are several chalets here belonging to people who come from Madrid."

The Hullero, as it descends, snorts and puffs, happy to be restrained by Chuchi's powerful arm.

The railway bank cuts a straight line right through the centre of an endless watercourse. There are some fields of hops protected by fencing.

"For tobacco", says Chuchi.

We approach Pedrún. There are more fields of hops, and a sawmill. Of the sawmill, Chuchi says:

"It belongs to Servando's father-in-law."

The poet Antonio Gamoneda keenly felt the lyricism of these lands, and wrote of them, from this very train:

> *We pass by villages of humble name*
> *—Pardavé, Pedrún, Matueca—,*
> *With houses whose noble walls*
> *Have been built upon little gardens.*
> *We see the silent streets, the mute church,*
> *Doors that are forever closed.*
> *This is what a village is:*
> *It's built with earth and humility*

"There's no station master here. That man's the postman, the other is with Works and Maintenance", explains Chuchi, pointing to us two men on the platform at Pedrún.

One of them comes up to the engine. Chuchi opens the door.

"A red ticket?", asks Chuchi. "No, I haven't one of those. They haven't given me one of those."

We continue. Black elms, poplars, and pastures alternate with low ridges and watercourses. There are lots of hops. Two women are bent over in one of the fields.

"It's good for smokers; I don't smoke", says Chuchi.

To the left is the village of Matueca, reddish and white, with a church belfry in which a stork has made its nest.

«A stork has made its nest in the belfry of Matueca's church»

"Ah, there's the stork's nest", says Chuchi, absolutely delighted. "The other day I saw six storks. They're so lovely they are! I wonder if there'll be one today. Is it true they only live for a year?"

The stork is in its nest, as if it were taking a bath. It puts its beak inside as if soaping itself. And behind its wing appear the head and neck of a baby. Chuchi is overcome with sheer joy.

"There it is! There it is!", he cries, but then is immediately affected by a sad thought, "Is it true they live for only a year; and that their babies never return to where they grew up?"

Matueca. Iglesia y ciguëña
FRAGUAS.

What Gamoneda wrote about the area in February holds true for this wet and grey day in June:

Straight and dark, the poplars fill
The banks with their serenity,
And, near to them, below the village,
The river flows, blue and lonely.

The Hullero is now carrying us at full gallop. To our left, between the row of elms and the river, extends a long, single-storied white building.

"What's that?"

"I don't know", answers Chuchi.

On its façade we read 'Residential Camp Pedro de Grado'.

«'The river flows, blue and lonely', wrote Gamoneda»

"Can you see well, Chuchi".

"My eyesight is already wearing out. I've got glasses over there", he says, pointing to the instruments panel where he says he keeps everything.

In the meadow more than a hundred cows are grazing.

"It's nice over there", says Chuchi. "That Basque chap who's on the television, that Amestoy person, should really have come here, you know. He was in Valmaseda. He took a photo of me on the 1502. He's a little chap, eh? Well, of course, next to me, what a fucking joke! It's just like the fox who goes after

356

the chicken: he doesn't leave a single bloody one."

Without stopping we pass Manzaneda, where there appears to be a group of half a dozen people waiting.

"It s just like that other television man, the one from Salas, you know the one who spoke about animals, Félix Rodríguez de la Fuente… It was just like when he was with the wolf", Chuchi continues saying.

358

"What a fucking joke! He put on that smile for all those who were cursing him". He imitates the howl of the wolf. "Uuuuuuuuuuuuuhhhhhhhh. A friend of mine couldn't stand the man, but then he cried for him afterwards."

We take a look over the edge of a ridge. The railway bank, the main road and the river all come together, though at different heights. The Hullero commands the upper level while, a few metres below, comes the road, hugging tightly to a slope of pines and poplars; then finally, at the bottom, there's the Torío river, opening up into a meandering expanse filled with pebbles. Above the river is a footbridge, made out of planks and rope.

"It's lovely, this branch line", says Chuchi. "On Sundays it's this full with people. I was here with the train on Sunday, it was this full with people."

A rustic beehive, made from corrugated iron, wood and cardboard, takes up much of a field to our left.

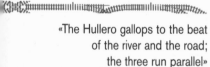

«The Hullero gallops to the beat of the river and the road; the three run parallel»

The Hullero gallops to the beat of the river and the road; the three run parallel. And then come the poplars of León. They line up in army formation along the banks of the Torío river, close together, luxuriant, swaying. Like creatures from the other side of Alice's mirror, they spill out into the fields beyond, in fours, in twos, in singles; they rise above the wooden fencing, hugely tall and skinny, marked by knots the size of storks' nests; they swell up on the hill tops, bushy, wide-necked, almost big-headed; they stretch out almost naked on the horizon, or else stand out against the sky, harmonious and symmetrical, like birds' feathers.

CHUCHI'S REMINISCENCES

GARRAFE. THE AUTHOR has now been travelling for more than ten hours, and he's as tired as if he'd been watching thirty films in a row. I look at my watch.

"Ten to Seven."

"We're doing well", according to Chuchi. "We'll be there by twelve minutes past."

The rhythm of the Hullero is the rhythm of Chuchi'. The one gallops at the dictates of the other, and the two of them are now advancing joyously and loquaciously.

"How he used to speak that man from Salas de los Infantes! I always used to like the way he smiled as he spoke. And I used to tell this friend: do you know why he smiles? On account of the wolf! Because it was on account of the wolf they used to say of him: look what a bastard, eh? He's happy to throw us all to the wolf, to the devil... and behind his back they all were calling him a bastard... When they showed that programme about the wolf! Did you see it? Uuuuuuhhhhhh!, and the sheperd was saying: 'The wolf's coming!' And I used to say: Look, look, when someone smiling like that, it's because they're saying: what a bastard. That's why he was smiling."

"How do you know?"

"I can imagine it! I can see him thinking: somebody will be calling me a bastard on account of the wolf, and so I'll smile. He was an intelligent man."

Fences, pastures, and poplars cover the fields and climb up the hills. A flock of sheep moves as if it were a single animal.

"And he said just before going away: 'Well, see you soon'. Someone told me he said that knowing he would never be back."

The nearer we get to León the more Chuchi speaks, and the faster he does so. All that he wasn't able to tell us before, he wants to say now.

"How he smiled that man! Uuuuuuhhhhhh! And that scene with the goat. No, it was a deer. When all the wolves followed her and set about her. No, it wasn't a goat, it was…"

Three powerful mastiffs with a greyish brown fur jump up as the Hullero passes, as if they had just pulled themselves away from some tasty flock. They follow the train for a good while, barking all the time by its side.

"The mother's still alive. She's in Santander, or somewhere up there, living with some sister of his. I used to love it when the wolfs ran after the deer. Oh, that was wonderful that was. And everyone used to like it. It was a really good programme. But it's true: he really did smile on account of the wolf. A day before he died a female wolf weighing some ninety kilos turned up, and this friend of mine from Vega del Pas said to me: 'It's that bastard Félix Rodríguez de la Fuente; he's the one to blame for this'. And yet when the man got killed in the plane crash, this friend almost cried, the old poof."

Chuchi wipes the steel wool across the Hullero's back. His monologue is unstoppable. The author suspects that Chuchi is trying to shake off some deep loneliness.

"Wasn't he some doctor or other?", he asks, not really interested in the answer, because he immediately continues talking. "Some mechanical fault in the plane, and the three of them were completely fucked. What a shame! How easy it is to take away a life! Everyone said what a great pity it was. He had a close friendship with this ticket collector from one of the Ansa buses, who killed himself, Juanito he was called, he used to work on the line to Espinosa. After the crash he stayed alive for at least two whole days. People were so sorry for him!"

We reach San Feliz. There are two brick buildings at this stop, isolated and clean; the largest, with two floors, is for passengers; the other is for goods.

Chuchi tells us:

"They used to load manure here, and unload

San Feliz de toues
FRAGUAS.

cement. But now they don't do either. León's the next stop."

The railway bank moves away from the Torío. The plain is becoming immense. These are the lands created by the Torío and the Bernesga as the two rivers converge on León.

There's a wealth of thyme. There are fields of barley. The poplars are as numerous as before. Dozens of cows graze in the meadows. In the distance can be seen the towers of León.

"Now we'll be able to ask the boss what Servando is called."

We're on the last stage of the journey, and Chuchi is getting everything out of his system:

«We reach San Feliz. There are two brick buildings at this stop»

"There was this stoker once who had a donkey, and this donkey was practically falling over with hunger. And he used to say to me: 'It's just not possible, I give him oats and barley, and he doesn't want to eat it'. But of course he wasn't going to eat it! The poor thing hadn't smelt oats and barley in his whole bloody life! And he kept on saying, it's just not possible, I give him barley and oats, and he doesn't want it."

The Hullero too seems to be acquiring a mind of its own; but Chuchi contains it.

"Another time we had some Germans who came to work on the railway, and they wanted to eat that

soft cheese from Burgos. The stoker removed the grease from the engine, and gave it them with wine. Come on, give us more wine, they said as they ate this. And the next day they were all ill in bed. They were engineers. The wine was very good, they said… the doctor didn't see them… had he done so, the stoker would still be in prison."

Chuchi brakes once more the Hullero. He continues speaking:

"There was this sergeant who bet lunch to the person who could make the Guardia Civil shift. When are you on duty? Such and such day. Someone had a brother-in-law who was a guard. And when the guard was about as far away from him as that little house over there, he started shouting for all he was worth. Oh, my God! Oh my God! And the brother-in-law asked what the hell was up with him. He got closer to him by about thirty of forty metres. What the hell's up, what's wrong with you? Ay, ay, I just can't shit! You fucking bastard, the guard said to him… But it was only a bet, it was only a bet, said the other."

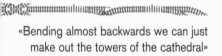

«Bending almost backwards we can just make out the towers of the cathedral»

Daisies and poppies now add their colours to León's verdant surroundings. Bending almost backwards we can just make out the towers of the cathedral, rising above the city's variegated skyline. Just a little bit more and we'll be in León.

THE LION OF SAINT MARK

T HERE'S SOMETHING CROSSING on the right side of the track. A dog, perhaps? Once we're closer
we can identify it as a rag. But, it's than a rag, it
seems something like a bundle wrapped in dark cloth,
something like a scarecrow or
even a big doll. The Hullero
whistles.

«The children meet up with another, larger group who are running around on a building site parallel to the track»

To our right, just above
us, looking over the railway
bank from a sand hill above
the boundary wall,   a child of eight or nine, wearing a peaked cap, watches, spellbound and naughtily
as the wheels of the train run over the rag doll.
What was he hoping would happen? Some complaint
from the driver? To see the engine jump up into
the air?

Slightly further on, other children are rushing
quickly over the tracks, and climbing like cats up the
wall. The Hullero whistles twice, almost screams.
The children meet up with another, larger group

who are running around on a building site parallel to the track. They watch us pass by.

Chuchi says:

"They're really a bad lot, they are! They throw stones and all. They're going to make me mad, they are!"

These children, thinks the author, are still free spirits like Chuchi himself, but soon they'll be tamed, disciplined, made cautious by the pressures of life. Then perhaps they'll emigrate to Bilbao.

The main road crosses the city right through its centre; the train surprises it from the back.

The back part of León is now all revealed: it's like a strange version of Venice, with a single iron canal along which the Hullero passes, scattering its panting sounds through courtyard wells, across flag-like rows of washing left to dry…

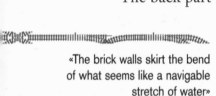

«The brick walls skirt the bend of what seems like a navigable stretch of water»

The railway bank is reduced to a canal on entering León. The urban gardens, grey walls, shared courtyards, brick walls, all skirt the bend of what seems like a navigable stretch of water.

To the right are the sports fields of the Maristas College, a place which brings back nostalgic memories for the author. A football has just landed on the railway line. The Hullero passes by, headed for Bilbao. The author, still barely an adolescent, leans on a window sill, watching the train and its carriages advancing

noisily. There are few things more seductive than a moving train. The clashing of its ironwork is as compelling as a heart beat. Suddenly, among the passengers, the author spots his friend Tomasín, with his big, red nose. They recognize each other simultaneously. How long is it since they've seen each other? Tomasín, amazed and excited, gets up and presses himself close against the window. The author opens his mouth, and raises his arm. But all is in vain. The painted brown sides of the train get in the way. The coaches continue on their journey. The pounding of iron against the track gets louder and louder, and then fades out. Where was Tomasín — that child boarder who had left the college so unexpectedly two years before— going to? To his village? Or had he already embarked, at so young an age, on the emigrant's path to exile?

We continue. Chuchi says:

"León's a very pretty capital… what with Ordoño II Street, La Condesa Avenue, the Hotel San Marcos…"

And on the last bridge through which the Hullero passes, we catch another glimpse of Venice — a Venice with a suburban character, humble and suffering… a simple bridge whose irregular arch, for all its architectural faults, has a romantic quality that brings to mind passing gondolas and vaporetti.

We enter the station. It's seven fifteen. Chuchi says:

"There's the tram that's going to Cistierna. We've arrived in good time."

The lazy ringing of a bell can be heard. The Cistierna tram, with its two blue carriages, whistles and leaves.

The Hullero puffs contentedly. It does so once
again after nearing the platform. The station master
is waiting. Chuchi says:

"He's from Mataporquera."

Chuchi wants to continue talking, and begs
Fernando to take a photo of him. Then he asks:

"What about a drink when I've finished? What
about a few drinks together?"

"Okay", we agree.

Three children, a woman, and two men are the
only people waiting for the Hullero. The station,
without being much larger than some of the other
important ones on the line, is not without its charm.
It was opened in 1923, following the completion
by the Industrial Railway Company of León of the
stretch in between León and Matallana. The author
particularly admires the main building's beautiful
eaves and roof (pitched on four sides in the upper,
central section, and on three sides in the wings) which
display that oxidized red colour typical of the local
clay. The name of the station features prominently
in dark letters set against yellow mosaic panels on
either side of the building. The ironwork canopy,
harmonious and elegant, rests on an arched framework
that, on reaching directly above the track, projects
into an upward-turned border. In addition there's a
small warehouse which shares its premises with the
urinals (a word absolutely characteristic of railway
stations), a depot with just three tracks, and —a

375

true relic of the past— a turntable once used by the steam trains.

The three of us jump out on to the platform. Fernando takes a photo of Chuchi, who straightens himself

and frowns for the benefit of the camera. Behind him, the Hullero seems almost to be breathing.

The station master approaches. He's skinny and neatly turned out. He carefully scrutinizes us. I explain what we've been doing, and show him the letter from the director of the FEVE. He smiles.

The Hullero, though resting on the track, has not stopped growling. And now it begins roaring unbearably, turning the station into an airport runway. The men from the goods van unload the parcels with a little cart. We hunch up our shoulders, and contort our faces into a futile grimace to try and block the noise. The station master shouts:

"Come inside, we'll be better off in there."

Chuchi asks him:

"What's Servando's name?"

The stationmaster, such an insignificant a figure alongside Chuchi, stiffens:

«There are a depot with just three tracks, and a turntable once used by the steam trains»

"Don Servando?"

"That's it!"

Chuchi goes back to the engine. Fernando stays on the platform, camera at the ready. Only the author goes into the office with the station master. The man is called Pedro Sánchez, he's from Mataporquera, and admits to being in love with León. "Here we've got everything, and sun as well." His wife is from León, "from the Calle Astorga itself." The author congratulates him on his wonderful staff, and praises

377

the railway in general. The station master cannot contain his enthusiasm:

"And it's the longest narrow track railway in Europe!", he exclaims.

We shake hands. And, just as the author is making for the door, Nazario and the railway worker who took over from Sergio Alvarez in Cistierna ask permission to enter. Nazario says:

"We have come to find out who's on tomorrow."

"Well, let's see: you…"

The station master goes up to his desk, and takes out a notebook.

"Today is the sixth", he says, thumbing through the pages. "Let's see: tomorrow Felipe and Nazario have their day off."

«We look towards the station building, as if to take in with a single glance the intense hours that are now behind us»

"And then we're on duty the following day."

"That's correct", says the station master.

The two men take their leave with military formality. And they say goodbye similarly to the author. Nazario smiles:

"At your service."

The author meets up with Fernando on the platform. Chuchi approaches us.

"Shall we go?", we ask.

"Not yet", he answers unhappily, "I've got to put the engine away."

"Will that take long?"

"I'll have to do a manoeuvre. Perhaps half an hour, an hour, something like that. Will you wait?"

We are tired, and make our apologies. We shake his hand.

"Have a good time", Chuchi says, but his voice has almost gone.

We go out on to the street. It's not raining, and —for the first time since leaving Bilbao— the glow from a hidden sun lights up part of the clouds. The station opens up on to a small, well shaded square, under threat from the unforgiving height of more than one modern building. It seems that the ground, after our long journey, is trembling beneath our feet. We turn our heads around. We look towards the station building, as if to take in with a single glance the intense hours that are now behind us. On the main façade are two coats-of-arms: that of León, and that of Vizcaya.

"We should have waited", says the author. "For Chuchi."

This first edition
by REY LEAR of
THE TRANSCANTABRIAN
was printed in
Spring of 2008